PELICAN BOOKS

A192

GREEK SCIENCE II

BY BENJAMIN FARRINGTON

BENJAMIN FARRINGTON

GREEK SCIENCE
ITS MEANING FOR US

II

THEOPHRASTUS TO GALEN

PENGUIN BOOKS
HARMONDSWORTH · MIDDLESEX

FIRST PUBLISHED IN PELICAN BOOKS 1949

Made and printed in Great Britain for Penguin Books Limited
by Northumberland Press Limited, Gateshead on Tyne

CONTENTS

INTRODUCTION

Part One of this book told the story of Greek Science from Thales to Aristotle and sought to define its significance for the modern world.

The period covered was from 600 to 322 B.C. This period is divided by the career of Socrates. The Presocratic period, it was argued, was the formative period of Greek science. It was the fruit in the intellectual field of a reasonably happy society which had launched a vigorous attack upon nature and had the picture in its mind of man as an ingenious and resourceful creature capable of indefinitely improving his conditions of life. As a sympathetic reviewer put it, 'the great theoretical advances were made by men who were well acquainted with the technical attack on nature, who developed therefrom a positive, enquiring, and to some extent experimental, attitude.'

The name of Socrates is associated with a shift of interest from natural philosophy to politics and ethics. This shift of interest represented a change in the condition of society. The confident picture of man as engaged in an attack on his natural environment had come to an end because of a social crisis. The crisis had been produced by the growth of the institution of slavery. The level of technical mastery over nature achieved at this time offered the Greeks the possibility of a cultivated leisure for a minority, and at the same time their geographical expansion offered them the possibility of enslaving weaker and more backward peoples. Slavery changed from a domestic and innocuous institution into an organized attempt to shift such heavy burdens as porterage, mining, and many agricultural and industrial processes on to the backs of alien chattel slaves. The ideal was established of the citizen as one who did not engage in manual work, and this carried with it the convenient theory that nature had intended other races of mankind to be unfit for citizenship and capable only of manual work.

One evil consequence of this was that control of techniques, knowledge of the processes of which is essential for many branches of science, passed into the hands of slaves, and an ideal of science was formed which was largely verbal and unrelated to practice. The *word* was the concern of the citizen, the *deed* the concern of the slave. As Sir Clifford Allbutt said of Plato, who is the great exponent of this phase of thought : 'Plato unfortunately despised the applications of science to the technical arts of man, not perceiving that from these arise some of the most luminous principles of academic science, nature being more ingenious and multiform and unexpected in operation than any laboratory.' (*Greek Medicine in Rome*, p. 84.)

Other evil consequences also followed. Slavery operated to make the rich richer and the poor poorer, concentrating wealth in the hands of those who had the money to invest in slaves, while it robbed the poor man as well as the rich of all initiative and enterprise in the face of nature. As a citizen the poor man too had his ideal of avoidance of manual labour. The poor citizen, therefore, constituted a proletariat that, unlike the modern proletariat, was divorced from the labour process. Too often he lived an idle parasitic life. Society had failed to organize him for the attack on nature or to give him the conditions under which he could pursue it for himself. Dispossessed and aimless, he too wanted to be carried on the back of the slave. Society tended to lose its character as an organization of citizens for common production. It became instead the arena within which rich and poor citizens fought for what was produced by the slave. Such were the social conditions under which interest shifted from natural philosophy to politics and ethics, that is, from the organization of society for the attack on nature to the attempt to prevent society from wearing itself out in a perpetual and futile civil war.

Lord Acton has a terrible phrase in his essays on *Freedom* about classical society: 'The issue of ancient politics was an absolute state planted on slavery.' Such is the ideal sketched in Plato's *Laws*. The oligarchy, reacting to the insecurity and instability of the times, became obsessed with the problem of providing sanctions by which the existing form of society might be maintained. The idea that increased control over nature could be won by human effort and could benefit mankind – the characteristic outlook of an earlier age – became less distinct: as how should it not, seeing that in the slow course of history more than a thousand years were to pass before the pattern of slave society was dissolved and technical progress became possible and fruitful for men? Accordingly the positive, enquiring, experimental attitude, which had accompanied the expansion of Greek civilization in the sixth and early fifth century, was abandoned as that civilization declined, and the desideratum became a code of laws buttressed by divine sanctions which should be unshakable. Sir Clifford Allbutt delights to find nature 'ingenious, multiform and unexpected'. But he is not stating the position quite accurately when he says that Plato did not perceive this. The unexpectedness of nature Plato perceived only too well. But since what he was looking for in nature was a pattern for the citizens of regularity, order and stability, nature on the whole filled Plato with dismay. Astronomy was the only natural science for which he had any enthusiasm, and, as we saw in our first volume, he could tolerate astronomy only on terms. These were that the behaviour of the heavenly bodies, so far from being multiform and unexpected, should be uniform and absolutely incapable throughout all eternity of springing any surprise on us whatsoever.

The formulation of an elaborate astral theology, which he knit into the fabric of his state, and belief in which he imposed by law, was the final outcome of Plato's thought. This point of view powerfully impressed Plato's pupil Aristotle in his youth, and he contributed greatly to elaborate and popularize it in his earlier writings. But later, after the foundation of his own school, he wrestled with success to restore a philosophy based on observation and experience of nature to a dominant position in the thought of his day. The degree of his success in this effort and, in particular, his tremendous achievement in the field of the biological sciences, were the last topics discussed in our first volume.

In this second part of our book we shall carry the story on from Theophrastus to Galen, that is to say, we shall begin again in the Lyceum of Athens after the death of Aristotle in 322 B.C. and end in Rome about A.D. 200. Our first task will be to describe the exciting advances in science made by Theophrastus and Strato, the immediate successors of Aristotle in the headship of the Lyceum. These advances one would certainly describe as epoch-making were it not that they failed to establish an epoch. That failure will be of as great interest to us as the achievement. Then we shall pass, with Strato, to Alexandria and follow the fate of science for some two hundred years under the Ptolemies, after which we shall shift our attention to Rome, the new mistress of the Mediterranean world.

But since we shall be vitally concerned in this second part of our book as in the first with *the meaning for us* of Greek science, we shall not be able to conclude with the death of ancient science but must also briefly consider its rebirth in the modern world. For this second birth of Greek science is a very extraordinary thing. It is only quite recently, according to the time-scale of the historian of civilization, that modern developments have made Greek science a matter of past history. When modern science began to show signs of vigorous life in the sixteenth century many of the pioneers felt, and rightly felt, that they were but resuming the old Greek tradition which had been interrupted for over a thousand years. Their new science was, in their eyes, a continuation of Greek science. The old Greek books which the invention of printing and the birth of modern scholarship were putting into their hands, were the best available, were, in fact, the most up-to-date books in various departments of knowledge. For Vesalius and Stevin in the sixteenth century the works of Galen and Archimedes were not historical curiosities. They were the best anatomical and mechanical treatises in existence. Even in the eighteenth century for Ramazzini, the founder of industrial medicine, Hippocratic medicine was still a living tradition, just as for Vico, the most profoundly original of all sociologists before Marx, Lucretius, with his Epicurean philosophy, could supply a basis for the new science of society. In one striking example the validity of a Greek text-book remained virtually unchallenged till our own century. A generation ago Euclid and geometry were still synonymous terms in English schools.

Why did Greek science die if it had still such vitality that it was capable of a second birth? This death and rebirth, or sleep and reawakening, constitute our problem. In the attempt at a solution of this problem we shall find the meaning for us of Greek science. Accordingly, after our journey from Athens via Alexandria to Rome, we shall ask why science, which had folded its hands for sleep, sprang to life again in the Low Countries, in Germany, in Italy, in France, in England.

In raising this question and seeking to answer it we shall pursue the same method as in our earlier volume. We shall not treat science in isolation but in its relation to the technical, social and political developments in the midst of which it grew.

BIBLIOGRAPHICAL NOTE

On the question of the causes of the general decline of ancient Society and its connection with the history of thought see F. Walbank, *The Causes of Greek Decline* (Journal of Hellenic Studies, Vol. LXIV, 1944), and *The Decline of the Roman Empire in the West*, Cobbett Press, 1946.

CHAPTER ONE

The Academy after Plato – The Lyceum after Aristotle – Theo-
phrastus and the criticism of teleology – Strato and the ex-
perimental method of research – Chemistry – Mechanics –
Music

★

THE ACADEMY AFTER PLATO

WHEN Plato died in 348/7 B.C. he left behind him a mystical
view of the universe set forth in his dialogues in a unique
combination of logic and drama. Its weakness was not that
it lacked support in argument but that it was not open to
correction from experience. It was not irrational so much as
unscientific. Its general character was dualistic, involving a
strong contrast between mind and matter, body and soul, god
and the world, time and eternity. The fundamental ideas
were derived from the religious doctrines of the Orphics as
refined and rationalized by the Pythagorean school. A doctrine derived from the Parsis, of an evil world-soul, appears
in the last dialogue, the *Laws*. This forerunner of the Christian devil is made responsible, among other things, for the
false doctrines of Plato's great rivals, the atomists. In opposition to their doctrines Plato himself teaches (1) a teleological
conception of nature, (2) belief in the transmigration of
souls, (3) a theory of a progressive deterioration of creation
(women being derived from inferior men and all the lower
animals from various types of human degeneracy), and (4)
the worship of the stars, especially the planets, as the highest
type of life.

Inside his own school his successors preserved his writings
but could do nothing to develop his thought. The mystical
beliefs we have enumerated were not susceptible of develop-

13

ment. Neither, indeed, was the Theory of Ideas. The great Cambridge scholar, Henry Jackson, writes : 'Metaphysics was, as has been well said, no more than a brief interlude in the history of Greek thought. It began with Plato and it ended with Plato.' It may be added that the hope, which modern scholarship has indulged, that Plato taught orally in the Academy a systematic philosophy different from that popularly expounded in the dialogues and recoverable by us from the study of Aristotle and other disciples, seems about to be abandoned as delusive. The one branch of teaching in the Academy really susceptible of development was mathematics, and here distinguished work continued to be done. Otherwise there is little or nothing. Plato was succeeded in the headship of the Academy by his nephew Speusippus (347–339). Jackson reminds us that he was a biologist with no taste for metaphysics. He is not a big figure in biology either. The next head was Xenocrates (339–314). Of him Jackson remarks : 'He was an amiable moralist who out of piety taught Plato's philosophy but did not understand it.' History has shown this to be the most persistent and prolific type of Platonist. Jackson proceeds : 'Then came other moralists, and after them epistemologists sceptically inclined. Thus within the school there was no one to preserve an intelligent tradition.' It is important to understand that throughout antiquity (and the school had a life of some nine hundred years) there was no real development, only a survival, of Platonism.

THE LYCEUM AFTER ARISTOTLE

The fortunes of the Lyceum, which Aristotle had founded as a break-away from the Academy, and where in the last thirteen years of his life (335–322) he achieved such amazing results in biological and historical research, were very different from those of the Academy. Aristotle's immediate successors, Theophrastus and Strato, were giants comparable with himself, and, though the school in Athens has no real history after them, it did not expire before it had handed on the torch to the Museum of Alexandria which kept it glowing pretty brightly at least for another hundred and fifty years. From the Lyceum and its offshoot, the Museum of Alexandria, proceed in the two hundred years which separate Aristotle from Hipparchus a succession of great organized treatises[1] on various branches of science – botany, physics, anatomy, physiology, mathematics, astronomy, geography, mechanics, music, grammar – which, largely modelled on the works of Aristotle himself and embodying and developing their spirit, constitute, with the addition of a few later contributions from men such as Dioscorides,[2] Ptolemy and Galen, the high water mark of the achievement of antiquity and the starting-point of the science of the modern world.

When Aristotle died he bequeathed to his followers a vast collection of material on physics, metaphysics, ethics, logic, politics and biology. These writings have been preserved to us, but they are not easy reading. We are told by an ancient writer that Aristotle gave two kinds of instruction. He gave formal instruction in the morning to regular students who had given proof of aptitude, attainment, zeal and industry. In the afternoon there were more popular lectures for a wider public. When Alexander the Great, whose tutor Aristotle

1. The Greek historian Polybius, who died 122 B.C. at the age of 82, remarked (*History* X, 47, 12): 'All branches of science have with us now made such progress that instruction in most of them has been systematized.'

2. As Dioscorides will not be mentioned again it may be noted here that he was the author (about A.D. 50) of a work *De Materia Medica* which lists and describes some 600 medicinal plants. The standard edition is in 3 vols. in the Teubner ed. by Max Wellman.

had been, heard a report that the subject matter of the morning lectures had been published he wrote to his teacher to protest. 'If you have made public what we have learned from you, how shall we be any better than the rest? Yet I had rather excel in learning than in power and wealth.' Aristotle told him not to worry. 'The private lessons,' he wrote, 'are both published and not published. Nobody will be able to understand them except those who have had the oral instruction.' This makes clear the general character of Aristotle's surviving writings. They constitute a body of formal doctrine in technical or semi-technical language demanding a determined apprenticeship. In style they are only occasionally fully polished. More often they are in the form of more or less elaborate lecture-notes.

Together with this body of material Aristotle bequeathed to his school a tradition of organized research. A library and laboratories were part of the equipment of his school and the objective, fact-finding character of the programme of research made possible, perhaps for the first time in history, a combination of direction of studies, of team-work, and of freedom of thought. That many hands collaborated in the compilation of the 158 constitutions of city-states which were to form a factual basis for his political philosophy is known. That many hands also contributed to the collection of materials for the biological treatises may be safely inferred. The freedom of thought which characterized the Lyceum is shown both by the rapid developments which took place there as well as by the divergent views of those who worked there at the same time. In the generation after Aristotle there was division of opinion in the school as to whether the active life or the theoretical was the better. An example both of division of work and of a new sense for the importance of the history of thought, however imperfectly developed as yet, is the assignment to various members of the school of the composition of histories of various branches of knowledge. To Theophrastus was assigned natural philosophy, to Eudemus mathematics and astronomy, to Xenocrates geometry, to Menon medicine. Dicaearchus wrote a history of Greek culture. Such was the institution which moulded the two great men with whom we shall be concerned in the rest of this chapter.

THEOPHRASTUS AND THE CRITICISM OF TELEOLOGY

Theophrastus was born at Eresos in the island of Lesbos about 373 B.C., being thus about twelve years Aristotle's junior. He was the son of a fuller, an important profession in those days. The fact is worth mentioning, just as it is worth mentioning that Aristotle's father was a doctor. Children born into the rentier's background, where the father derived his revenues from estates run by a slave bailiff, had not so good a chance of understanding the practical aspect of science. Theophrastus, in fact, showed considerable understanding of the fact that science ought not only to give logical answers to puzzling questions but also lead to desired results in practice. He began his higher education, as Aristotle had done, under Plato at the Academy. After Plato's death he joined Aristotle at the Lyceum, where he was his pupil and friend and finally his successor. Since Aristotle died in his sixties while Theophrastus lived to be eighty-five, he outlived his teacher by some thirty-five years. The years (322–287) during which Theophrastus was head of the Lyceum were extraordinarily fruitful for science. This is a fact which has not always been recognized. Indeed, until the researches of the last fifty years had advanced sufficiently to reverse the established opinion, Theophrastus remained in the shadow of his great teacher. Now it is certain that we must see in

him an independent figure as original as he was industrious.
He had the advantage of living and working till he was
about fifty with one of the greatest figures in the history of
science. He repaid the debt by making striking advances
on his teacher. If all his works had survived they would,
on a rough estimate, have made a collection of about fifty
volumes of fifty thousand words each. What now survives
would make four or five such volumes. It will serve to
enable us to indicate the advances he made in three main
spheres – metaphysics, biology, and the doctrine of the four
elements.

Among the surviving works of Theophrastus is a short
writing bearing the title *Metaphysics*. Its length – it occupies
only nineteen pages in the edition of Ross and Forbes – is no
indication of its importance or its difficulty. It is difficult
because it belongs to that class of technical writings which
could only be fully understood by those thoroughly con-
versant with the teaching of the Lyceum. It is important
because it raises questions fundamental for the constitution
of a science of nature based on observation. Theophrastus
distinguishes the study of First Principles, that is Metaphysics, from the study of nature, which the Greeks called
Physics, and seeks to define the limitations and connections
of these two enquiries. Nature, he tells us, is more multi-
farious and disorderly and its study depends on the evidence
of the senses. First Principles are definite and unchanging as
being concerned with the objects of reason, which are without motion or change. Theophrastus adds that men regard
the latter as a greater and more dignified study. Obviously
he is not satisfied with this conclusion, his purpose
being to clear the way for a new advance in observational
science.

It will be remembered that Aristotle, in his *Metaphysics*,
had prepared the way for his biological studies by his doc-

trine of 'immattered form' (Vol. I, p. 115). The general notion which this doctrine yields is that organic nature is the result of a process in which a power called Nature or God imposes on Matter, so far as possible, certain Forms conceived of as being somehow good. The human form, for instance, provided it be masculine, Greek and free, is something good. But Nature cannot always impose anything so fine on Matter. Hence the less perfect forms of women, non-Greeks and slaves, and, at a greater remove, of animals and even plants. But, though Nature is not all-powerful, it is legitimate and necessary to ask always in the study of her works *at what good she was aiming* and to assume as a principle that *she does nothing in vain*.

It is this whole conception that Theophrastus wishes to subject to fresh analysis. First he asks whether there are any First Principles, any objects of reason, apart from mathematics. He has none to adduce. But this leaves him with the further question whether the principles of mathematics are adequate also to explain Nature. This he denies for two very interesting reasons. First he says that mathematical principles themselves seem to be a human contrivance. They have been invented by men in the process of investing things with figures, shapes and ratios, and have no independent existence. Secondly the principles of mathematics seem incapable of imparting life and motion to things.

This second objection leads him to an interesting speculation which goes to the root of idealist philosophy. In the Presocratic materialist philosophy motion had been regarded as the mode of existence of matter. Plato, however, had taught the view that matter is essentially inert and that its motion requires explanation. This explanation he had attempted to give by assigning Soul as the cause of motion, thus introducing the dualistic conception on which all idealism ultimately rests. Aristotle had wrestled with the problem bequeathed to philosophy by Plato, namely how Soul, itself unmoved, can be the source of motion in other things. He had answered it by an analogy. Soul attracts Matter in the way in which a beloved person attracts a lover. The whole motion and activity of nature, in particular the revolution of the heavens, is nothing but a striving of Matter to approximate to Soul. Theophrastus now raises this whole question, mentions Aristotle's solution only to reject it, and asks in his turn whether any explanation for the motion of the heavens is really necessary. He goes back in effect to the Presocratic position. 'To be moved,' he writes, 'is proper both to nature in general and to the celestial system in particular. Hence also, if activity is of the essence of each natural object, and a particular thing when it is active is also in movement, as in the case of animals and plants (which if they are not in movement are animals and plants only in name), it is clear that *the celestial system also in its rotation is in accordance with its essence, and if it were divorced from this and were at rest it would be a celestial system only in name* ; for the rotation is a sort of life of the universe. Surely, then, if the life in animals does not need explanation or is to be explained only in this way, may it not be the case that in the heavens too, and in the heavenly bodies, movement does not need explanation or is to be explained in a special way?'

Having in this way swept aside the whole effort to create a theology, in the manner of Plato and Aristotle, from what they thought they knew (or chose to believe) about the motions of the heavenly bodies, Theophrastus proceeds in his last chapter to lay hands on the Ark of the Covenant, the teleological principle itself. 'With regard to the view that all things are for the sake of an end and nothing is in vain, the assignation of ends is in general not easy, as it is usually stated to be.' This protest against the glib assertion of the universality of purpose and the rashness with which some philosophers assign ends to things, he backs up with powerful arguments. What is the purpose, he asks, of inundations and refluxes of the sea, of droughts and floods? In animals, what is the use of the breasts in the male or of hair in certain parts of the body? But the most important and most conspicuous failure of purpose in Nature is in connection with the nutrition and birth of animals. The presence or absence of the conditions under which either can occur are due to mere coincidences. If nature means to provide them for animals she should do so uniformly and always. Then, without mention of Aristotle's name, he selects from him examples of the teleological mode of explanation only to reject them. His final opinion is that if science is to make progress this reckless teleology must be checked. He concludes with these words: 'We must try to set a limit to the assigning of final causes. This is the prerequisite of all scientific enquiry into the universe, that is into the conditions of existence of real things and their relations with one another.'

It was the opinion of the Swiss botanist and historian of science, Senn, that the critique of teleology which Theophrastus conducts with such firmness in his *Metaphysics* could be applied with confidence to the dating of the various parts of his botanical treatises which have been preserved for us. The botanical works which have come down to us are two, the *History of Plants* in nine books, and the *Causes of Plants* in six. Senn's opinion, in which he has the support of Brunet and Mieli, is that this division of the botanical writings is not due to the author but represents the work of editors in the Museum of Alexandria, who, distinguishing in the writings of Theophrastus passages in which he employs the teleological principle from passages in which he carefully avoids it, grouped them in separate volumes. The

Causes of Plants would thus represent a collection of the earlier writings of Theophrastus in which, being still under the influence of Aristotle, who 'surpassed all other natural philosophers in the discovery of causes' (Diogenes Laertius, V, 32), he acquiesced in the teleological mode of explanation, while the *History of Plants* would represent the works composed after the critique of teleology we have just examined in the *Metaphysics*.

Senn's emphasis on the Theophrastan critique of teleology is to be commended but the conclusions he bases on it cannot be accepted. As the latest enquirer, Regenbogen, has pointed out, Theophrastus proposed only to set a limit to the use of the teleological principle, not to dispense with it entirely. What he wants is not a blunt rejection of the principle but a sceptical reserve in its application. He would seem, indeed, to have arrived at the very modern conclusion that the assumption of purpose in order to explain phenomena is inadmissible, while the collection of any evidence that might seem to point to design is a legitimate activity of science. That this is the truer account of the attitude of Theophrastus is borne out by the fact that the idea of purpose is not completely excluded from the *History*, nor indeed is the criticism of teleology absent from the *Causes*. There is no sufficient reason to reverse the tradition, which makes of the *History* the earlier work. Senn had had to reverse this order to maintain his thesis. The truth would appear to be that criticism of teleology, which is not absent even from the pages of Aristotle,[3] becomes freer and bolder in Theophrastus but is to be regarded rather as a sign of his sceptical scientific temper, operative throughout his career, than of a crisis of thought occurring some years after the death of Aristotle, a crisis which found him a teleologist and left him an empiric.

3. *Parts of Animals*, IV, 2, 8.

There is no evidence of a crisis. There is evidence everywhere of his sceptical reserve.

So much for the critique of teleology as it shows itself in the biological treatises. We cannot discuss these treatises in any detail, but before we leave them we should indicate what was probably the greatest contribution to knowledge made by Theophrastus. This consists in his firm drawing of the distinction between the animal and the vegetable kingdom. In our earlier volume (p. 119) we drew attention to the famous passage in Aristotle (*Parts of Animals*, IV, 10) in which, following Plato, he had advanced the theory that animals were descended from men. If we had there followed Aristotle further we should have found that he went on to derive plants from animals. He held a theory not of evolution but of degeneration, from man through animals to plants. All that concerns us in that theory now is that it contains no clear differentiation between animals and plants. Aristotle had not succeeded in defining the difference. In the organization of research in the Lyceum Aristotle had charged himself with the task of bringing order into the animal kingdom and had left the plants to his disciple. He had, however, unwittingly created an initial obstacle to the establishment of a sound science of botany by drawing too close a parallel between the parts of animals and of plants. Correctly observing the *functional* analogies between various parts of animals and plants he deduced therefrom a *morphological* analogy which does not hold.

It is with the clearing up of this confusion that the first chapter of the first book of the *History* is concerned. Theophrastus fastens at once on the fundamental difference between the parts of animals and of plants. In animals we mean by a part something that is permanent when once it has appeared, unless it be lost by disease, age or injury. But in plants many parts – flower, catkin, leaf and fruit – are renewed and die every year. The new shoot must also be included in this category, for plants make fresh growth both above and below ground every year. If we accept all these as parts of the plant, as in fact we must, then the number of parts in a plant (unlike the parts of animals) is both indeterminate and constantly changing. Perhaps, then, he continues, introducing his divergence from his master again without mention of his name, we should not expect to find a complete correspondence between the parts of plants and animals and should even make bold to include their fruits as parts of plants although we do not include their young as parts of animals. He rounds off his exposition with these strong words: 'It is a waste of time to force comparisons where they do not exist and constitutes an obstacle to our special branch of knowledge.' In this masterly but unobtrusive style did Theophrastus separate the animal from the vegetable kingdom and establish the science of botany at a level above which it was not destined to rise till modern times.

Equally masterly is his criticism of the traditional doctrine of the four elements. For all the ancient schools it was accepted doctrine that, whatever the ultimate structure of matter might be, it presented itself to human observation under four primary forms, Earth, Water, Air and Fire, each distinguished from the rest by the possession of certain qualities. In the Aristotelian doctrine Earth was dry and cold, Water wet and cold, Air wet and hot, Fire dry and hot. The Dry, the Wet, the Hot, the Cold were Forms, which being impressed in pairs on undifferentiated Matter brought into existence the four primary substances out of which the universe was made. Each of the elements had one of its qualities in common with another, and this sharing of a quality was held to facilitate their transformation into one another – a process supposed to be continually going on in nature. Such was the traditional view as shaped by Aristotle. The capacity of Theophrastus to transcend and deepen this view is proved by a fragment, twenty-three pages in length, part of a treatise *On Fire*. The opening passage is of greatest importance for us. A translation, in slightly condensed form, follows :

Of all the elements Fire has the most remarkable properties. Air, Water and Earth can only change into one another, none of them can generate itself. Fire can not only generate itself but extinguish itself. A small fire can generate a large one, a large one can put out a small one. (Theophrastus explains what he means by this later. A lamp held over a fire goes out.) Furthermore most ways of generating fire seem to involve force. Examples are the striking of flint on steel, the rubbing together of fire-sticks, and the generation of fire from air by the gathering and collision of clouds. The contrast between the forcible generation of fire and the natural change of the other three elements into one another involves a remarkable consequence for us. We can generate fire, we cannot generate the other three. Even when we dig a well we do not bring water into being, we merely make it visible by collecting it from a scattered state. But the greatest and most important difference has yet to be mentioned. The other elements are self-subsistent, they do not require a substratum. Fire does – at least such fire as is perceptible by our senses. This is true whether we include light in our concept of fire or not. If we include light, then light requires air or water as a medium. If we do not include light, still both the fire of flame and that of a glowing coal exist in a substratum. Flame is burning smoke. A coal is an earthy solid. It makes no difference whether the fire is in the sky or on earth. In the first case fire is burning air, in the second case it is either all the three other elements burning or two of them. Speaking generally fire is always coming into being. It is a form of motion. It perishes as it comes into being. As it leaves its substratum it perishes itself. That is what the ancients meant when they said that fire is always in search of nutriment. They saw that it could not subsist of itself without its material. What is the sense then of calling Fire a First Principle if it cannot subsist without some material? For, as we have seen, it is not a simple thing nor can it exist before its substrate and material. One might of course assert that in the outermost sphere there exists a kind of fire which is pure and unmixed heat. If so it could not burn, and burning is the nature of fire.

It is difficult to bring the scientific advance registered in this passage home to the reader without a long quotation from Aristotle, for which we have no room. It derives its special character from its accumulation of careful observations of both natural and artificial processes and the closeness with which the reasoning clings to the observed facts.

The great novelty of this will be apparent to anyone who will go to Aristotle's treatise *On Coming To Be and Passing Away* and read the first four or five chapters of Book II. There he will find a great deal of logic and very little observation. The comparison of the two passages will bring home to him the difference between studying natural philosophy through the eye of reason or the eye of sense. It is clear that great changes are being effected in the Lyceum, but changes which are in the line of Aristotle's own development. The practice of observation which he had himself employed with such success in the field of biology (see Vol. I, pp. 117, 118) is now being extended by his disciple to the study of inorganic and inanimate matter. It is clear also that the new observational method is not destined to be long in sweeping away the physical conceptions which Aristotle had brought with him from the Academy. The observation that fire cannot exist without a substratum, that fire is something burning, leads at once to the theory that fire is not an element but rather a compound, and then to the further suggestion that the Hot and the Cold are not really principles but attributes. These new developments mark the end of the Aristotelian physics and prepare the way for Strato.

In his *Metaphysics* Theophrastus drops the remark that in our endeavour to understand the behaviour of matter 'we must in general proceed by making reference to the crafts and drawing analogies between natural and artificial processes' (8*a*, 19, 20). In our first volume we have written at length on the importance of this approach for the Greek pioneers of science. What Theophrastus means by it is abundantly illustrated by his fragment *On Fire* as well as by others of his writings. In the twenty-odd pages of this treatise there are hundreds of observations both of natural and artificial processes. When we study them closely we see that attention to the artificial processes involved in the crafts sharpens his observation of natural processes and suggests their explanation. Thus, above, in making his point that fire generally requires force or violence for its generation, he groups in one sentence the artificial means by which men make fire and the natural phenomenon of lightning, which gets its explanation thereby. Later on he compares the red colour sometimes assumed by the light of the sun with the red flame of fresh green logs and decides that the flame from green logs gets its colour from the extra moist and earthy element contained in green logs as compared with seasoned ones and that the sun gets its reddish hue whenever 'the air is thick'.

STRATO AND THE EXPERIMENTAL METHOD OF RESEARCH

This constant reference back and forwards between observations of natural and artificial phenomena is the root from which the technique of experiment has grown. It does not yet, of course, constitute such a technique. But with the name of Strato we reach the point at which Greek science fully establishes a technique of experiment, and we may pause for a moment to retrace some of the steps by which such a decided and important advance in scientific method was achieved. The Swiss botanist, Senn, who has made such important contributions to the history of scientific thought, can also help us here. In an examination of the Hippocratic writings he makes a distinction between two types of comparison found there. Very commonly we find comparisons drawn between the physiological processes being investigated and common occurrences of practical life. The writer, for instance, makes a remark like this : 'It is just as when cold water is added to boiling water, the water stops boiling.' Here a phenomenon in medicine which the writer is trying to understand is illustrated by reference to a common experience, but there is no suggestion that the pupil should go and try the experiment. Less frequently, however, we come upon a formula of this kind : 'If you do so and so you will find that such and such is the case,' where it seems clear that the student is invited and expected to repeat the experiment for himself.

A good example of experiment of this sort is found in *Ancient Medicine* (chap. xxii). The writer is there impressing on the student that there is a relation between the structure of the internal organs of the body and the functions they perform. He lays down the general principle that the functioning of the internal organs, being hidden, can best be studied by examination of unenclosed objects of similar shape. 'Now which structure is best adapted to draw and attract to itself fluid from the rest of the body, the hollow with the wide opening, the solid and round, or the hollow and tapering?

I take it the best adapted is a wide hollow vessel with a tapering mouth. These principles must be learned from external and visible objects. For example, if you open the mouth wide you will not draw in any fluid ; but if you protrude and purse your lips, or if you press your lips together and insert a tube you could easily suck up anything you like. Again, cupping instruments, which are broad and tapering, are so designed on purpose to draw and suck up blood from the flesh. There are many other examples of the same kind. Now of the parts within the human frame, the bladder, the head and the womb are of this shape. These obviously attract powerfully and are always full of fluid from without.'

Here is something which is plainly different from a mere reference to a familiar occurrence used by way of illustration in the course of an argument. Here a confirmatory action is demanded of the listener, a repetition of the experience. It is still rudimentary in development but it is genuine experiment. This method, which among the earlier schools is most clearly to be detected with the Pythagoreans, is only occasionally employed by the other Presocratics, or the Academy, or even the Peripatetics down to and including Theophrastus. It is with the successor of Theophrastus, Strato, that it comes to sudden flower.

Considering the importance of this man we know miserably little about him. We know that he was born in Lampsacus, that he lived some time in the King's palace at Alexandria before being summoned to the headship of the Lyceum at Athens, and that he was head of the institution from 287 to 269. He must already have been a famous man before he became head of Aristotle's school, otherwise he would not have been summoned by the first Ptolemy (Soter) to supervise the education of his son, the second Ptolemy (Philadelphus), which was the occasion of his residence in Alexandria. He can hardly have been under forty years of age and may have been fifty when he took up his post in Athens. The names of about forty of his writings are listed for us by Diogenes Laertius, but time has robbed us of them all, and modern scholarship has yet to complete the task of giving us a scientific edition of the fragments of his works that can be gleaned from later writers.

We learn, however, from Polybius the historian, who lived about a hundred years later, that he was known in antiquity by the special name of The Physicist (of course in the old Greek meaning of the term, i.e. the natural philosopher). Cicero explains the choice of this title when he tells us that Strato 'abandoned ethics, which is the most necessary part of philosophy, and devoted himself to the investigation of nature'. It is unlikely that Cicero would be the only one to condemn such a choice, and that it brought Strato under criticism in his own day is rendered pretty certain by the further statement of Polybius that 'his critical and polemical writings were brilliant, but his exposition of his own ideas dull'. The reader will probably agree, when we have finished our account of the work of Strato, that Polybius's last word 'dull' should be interpreted 'too severely scientific to suit the temper of the age'. The concluding words of the brief notice of Diogenes appear to throw a little more light on this point. He tells us that Strato 'excelled in every branch of learning but most of all in that which is styled the philosophy of nature, *a branch of philosophy more ancient and serious than the others*'. We shall surely not be wrong in seeing in these remarkable words Strato's own defence of his preference for natural philosophy over ethics and politics. Strato would call natural philosophy more ancient as being characteristic of the older schools before Socrates turned philosophy away from nature to man. He would call it more serious as being connected rather with the basic arts on which life itself depends than with the arts which are the adornment of a decadent civilization. We have quoted in our first volume (p. 84) the opinion of the Presocratics that 'the arts which make the most serious contribution to human life are those which blend their own power with that of nature, like medicine, agriculture and gymnastics'. This description is intended to contrast them with those arts that merely imitate nature without altering her, like painting or music. No doubt we have struck here something fundamental in the outlook of Strato whose experimental attitude to science involved not merely passive observation of, but active interference with, the processes of nature. Strato was fully conscious of the practical applications of his physical theories. The ancient writer who preserves the best account of them introduces them with the words: 'They can provide us with the most fundamental requisites of a civilized existence.'

In the wreck of Strato's writings it was difficult to prove the completeness with which he had conceived the idea and established the practice of experimental research until a great discovery was made in 1893 by the penetrating genius of Hermann Diels. Among the surviving works of Greek science a prominent place is occupied by the *Pneumatics* of Hero of Alexandria, a work which dates in all probability from the first century of our era. In the opening pages of this text-book is contained a scientific theory of the nature of the vacuum of an obviously advanced kind. It is empirical in method, has a fixed terminology, and implies a unified physical system. Diels, who was the first to analyse the special qualities of this opening section of the work, also successfully claimed the bulk of it for Strato. Of this passage we proceed to offer the reader a somewhat condensed translation. It forms the best introduction to the genius of Strato.

The science of pneumatics was held in high regard of old

by philosophers and engineers, the former logically deducing its principles, the latter determining them by experimental tests. What we have felt constrained to do in this book is to give an orderly exposition of the established principles of the science and add thereto our own discoveries. We hope in this way to be of service to future students of the subject.

Before we come, however, to the particulars of our exposition there is a general topic to be discussed, namely the nature of the vacuum. Some writers emphatically deny its existence. Others say that under normal conditions there is no such thing as a continuous vacuum, but that small vacuums exist in a scattered state in the air, water, fire and other bodies. This is the opinion to which we should adhere. We now proceed to show by experimental tests that this is a true account of the matter.

We must first correct a popular illusion. It must be clearly grasped that vessels which are generally believed to be empty are not really empty but are full of air. Now air, in the opinion of the natural philosophers, consists of minute particles of matter for the most part invisible to us. Accordingly if one pours water into an apparently empty vessel, a volume of air comes out equal to the volume of water poured in. To prove this make the following experiment. Take a seemingly empty vessel. Turn it upside-down, taking care to keep it vertical, and plunge it into a dish of water. Even if you depress it until it is completely covered no water will enter. This proves that air is a material thing which prevents the water entering the vessel because it has previously occupied all the available space. Now bore a hole in the bottom of the vessel. The water will then enter at the mouth while the air escapes by the hole. But if before you bore the hole you lift the vessel vertically out of the water and turn it up and examine it you will see that the interior of the vessel has remained perfectly dry. This constitutes the demonstration that air is a bodily substance.

Air becomes wind by being set in motion. Wind is simply

air in motion. If after boring a hole in the bottom of the vessel and plunging the vessel into the water you keep your hand near the hole you will feel the wind streaming out of the vessel. This is simply the air being driven out by the water. You must not then suppose that a continuous vacuum is among the things that exist, but that small vacuums exist in a scattered state in air, water and other bodies. This must be understood in the sense that the particles of air, while in contact with one another, do not completely fit into one another. They leave empty spaces between, as does the sand on the beach. The grains of sand may be compared to the particles of air, and the air between the grains of sand is to be compared to the vacuum between the particles of air.

The consequence of this physical structure of the air is that if an external force be applied air is capable of being compressed and of settling into the empty spaces, its particles being crushed together in a way contrary to nature. On the relaxation of the pressure, owing to the elasticity of the particles, it resumes its former state. Similarly, if the application of any force results in the separation of the particles from one another and the creation of larger empty spaces between them than is natural under normal conditions, then their tendency is to draw together again. The reason for this is that the motion of the particles becomes rapid through the void, there being nothing to impede or resist it until the particles get into contact with one another again.

The following is an experimental demonstration of the above theory. Take a light vessel with a narrow mouth, suck the air out and take your hands away. The vessel will remain suspended from your lips because the void will tend to pull the flesh in to occupy the empty space. This makes it clear that a continuous void had been created in the vessel. Here is another proof of this. Medical doctors have glass vessels with narrow mouths which they call 'eggs'. When they wish to fill them with a liquid they suck the air out, put their fingers over the mouth and invert the vessel in the liquid. The liquid is then drawn in to fill the empty space, although an upward motion is unnatural for a liquid.

Let us now return to those who absolutely deny the existence of the void. It is of course possible for them to discover many arguments in reply to what has been said and in the absence of any experimental demonstration their logic may appear to have an easy victory. We shall therefore show them, by phenomena which can be brought under observation, two facts: (1) that there is such a thing as a continuous void, but that it exists only contrary to nature, and (2) that in accordance with nature void also exists, though only in small scattered quantities. We will further show them that under pressure bodies fill up these scattered vacuums. These demonstrations will allow no loophole of escape for these verbal gymnasts.

For our demonstration we shall require a metal sphere, of a capacity of about four pints, made of metal sheeting of such thickness as to resist any tendency to collapse. The sphere must be air-proof. A copper tube, a pipe with a narrow bore, must be inserted in the sphere in such a way that it does not touch the spot diametrically opposite the point of entry but leaves room for the passage of water. The pipe should project about three inches from the sphere. The part of the sphere around the point of insertion of the pipe must be strengthened with tin solder so that the pipe and the sphere present a continuous surface. There must be no possibility that air forced into the sphere by blowing can escape by any crack.

Now let us analyse in detail the implications of the experiment. There is air in the sphere from the beginning as in all vessels popularly called empty, and the air fills the whole of the enclosed space and presses continuously against the containing wall. Now according to the logicians, since there is absolutely no unoccupied space, it should be impossible to introduce water or more air unless some of the air already contained in the vessel be displaced. Further, if the attempt were made to force air or water in, the vessel being full should burst before admitting it. Very well. What in fact happens?

One who puts his lips to the pipe can blow a great quantity of air into the sphere without any of the contained air escaping. This happens as often as the experiment is repeated, and it constitutes a clear proof that the particles of air in the sphere are compressed into the vacuums between the particles. This contraction is contrary to nature, being the consequence of the forcible intrusion of air. Again if, after blowing, one stops the pipe quickly with one's finger, the air remains the whole time compressed in the sphere. But on the removal of the finger the air that was forced in rushes out noisily and violently, being expelled by the expansion of the air within owing to its elasticity.

If the reverse experiment be tried, a great quantity of air in the sphere can be sucked out without any other air getting in to replace it, as we saw before in the case of the 'egg'. This experiment conclusively demonstrates that the formation of a continuous vacuum takes place in the sphere. From this it follows that vacuums are interspersed in the interstices of the particles of air and that when force is applied the air suffers a compression contrary to nature into the vacuums. The existence of a continuous vacuum contrary to nature has already been shown by the adherence of the light vessel to the lip and by the example of the doctor's 'egg'. Many other experiments about the nature of the void might be adduced but these may suffice, for they depend on the evidence of observable phenomena. Summing up then we may say that every body consists of tiny particles of its material between which are interspersed vacuums smaller than its parts. It is only by an abuse of language that it can be maintained that, in the absence of force, there is absolutely no void but everything is full of air or water or some other substance, and that it is only in so far as one of these substances departs that another can enter in to occupy the empty space.'

A reviewer of one of my books writing in *The Journal of Roman Studies* (Vol. XXXI, 1941, p. 149) categorically states 'experimentalism as a systematic theory was unknown to Antiquity : it is a product of the Renaissance '. In face of the quotation we have given, and the quotation of course does not stand alone, this writer's pronouncement must be declared unfounded. In Strato we find the exponent of a systematic experimentalism which represents the culmination of a practice occasionally observed earlier with the Pythagoreans, with Empedocles, with Anaxagoras, with some doctors of the Hippocratic school, an experimentalism which has got so far that it involves the construction of special apparatus for the solution of a special type of problem, and which is backed up by the explicit assertion of the primacy of experiment over logical demonstration.

Among the disciples of Strato was an Alexandrian physician, Erasistratus, of whom we shall have something more to say later on. Among the fragments of his writings we find a striking expression of the zeal for natural philosophy which consumed the men of this age who came under the influence of the Lyceum. The passage is from Galen's *Scripta Minora* (II, 17, ed. Müller) and is quoted in Heidel's *Heroic Age of Science* (p. 53) : 'Those who are altogether unaccustomed to research are at the first exercise of their intelligence befogged and blinded and quickly desist owing to fatigue and failure of intellectual power, like those who without training attempt a race. But one who is accustomed to investigation, worming his way through and turning in all directions, does not give up the search, I will not say day or night, but his whole life long. He will not rest, but will turn his attention to one thing after another which he considers relevant to the subject under investigation until he arrives at the solution of his problem.'

Lest anybody should suppose that the research envisaged by Erasistratus in this exquisite passage was of the kind that can be carried on entirely in the head, as Parmenides recommended and Plato practised, let us quote *en passant* one of the experiments of this great physiologist. Remember he is attempting to investigate the processes of life and is concerned with the significance of respiration, as Empedocles was long before him in his experiment with the toddy-lifter (see Vol. I, p. 51). But how marvellous a development the technique of experiment has undergone! Worming his way through his problem and turning in all directions Erasistratus has arrived at an experiment which anticipates the famous achievement of Sanctorius (1561–1636). Sanctorius, in an experiment finely described by Singer (*A Short History of Medicine*, p. 108), lived some time suspended in a balance of his own devising in order to investigate changes of weight in the human body. Similarly Erasistratus put a bird in a cage and weighed it, left it without food and weighed it again together with the droppings only to find a considerable loss of weight. He recommends the repetition of this as a stock experiment (Diels, *Anonymi Londinensis*, p. 62ff.).[4] Here the exact measurement implied by the weighing should be noted. So perfect, and so various in its applications, has the experimental method become.

If we return now to Strato we shall find abundant evidence of how he too wormed his way through and turned in every direction in his efforts to solve his problems. In the passage which I quoted above I used a shortened version in order to concentrate attention on the main experiment with the sphere. But if we turn to the full text we shall find the record of many supplementary experiments. In advancing the theory of the presence in all substances of vacuums dispersed between the particles, Strato hazards the suggestion that the 'diamond' may be the one substance which does not contain void. He says it is indestructible by fire and offers such resistance to blows as to embed itself in the hammer or the

4. See also the new edition, *The Medical Writings of Anonymus Londinensis*, by W. H. S. Jones, C.U.P. 1947 (p. 127).

anvil. A diamond, of course, will split under the blow of a hammer along the planes of its crystal. One would like a longer account of what tests Strato had here employed. Possibly he had found small particles of emery or corundum embedded in hammer or anvil. The word translated 'diamond' above would be equally applicable to these. When he mentions the elasticity of the air he illustrates his meaning by comparison with the behaviour of horn shavings and a dry sponge. The evidence derived from light vessels which hang from the lip when the air has been sucked out is reinforced by the example of the heavier cupping-glass in which rarefaction has been produced not by suction but by heat.

This leads on to a striking section in which the action of heat on various bodies is discussed. It is pointed out that if heat is applied to coal so as to produce coke, the coke appears to the eye to be of the same bulk as the coal but is found on weighing to be lighter. Here again is evidence of the exact measurement of phenomena. The loss of weight is ascribed to the transformation of coal under the action of fire into three substances of differing densities, classed as fire, air and earth. There follows an interesting comment on the action of fire on water. In order to keep our historical perspective right it may be well to remind the reader that it was not until 1615 that air and steam were specifically distinguished and the practical conclusion drawn that there were potentialities in steam pressure of much greater magnitude than were to be found in air pressure. It was the work of Cardan (1501–1576) and Porta (1538–1615) that led to the decisive pronouncement of Solomon de Caus (1576–1630) that steam is evaporated water and that upon cooling the vapour returns to its original condition. Now Strato did not succeed in drawing the distinction between steam and air, but he does record explicitly the conclusion that 'the steam from a heated cauldron is simply rarefied water passing into "air"'. He could not have known how much this vapour differs from the air we breathe.

Strato used his theory of the discontinuous void in things to help in the interpretation of many phenomena. It has an obvious bearing on the problem of differences in density of various substances. It is invoked by him to assist in the interpretation of the action of the sun's rays in the evaporation of moisture and the phenomena of dew and hot springs. But perhaps its most suggestive application is to the problem of the propagation of light. 'If vacuums did not exist neither light nor heat nor any other material force would be able to penetrate the substance of water or air or any other body. How, for instance, could the sun's rays get to the bottom of a bucket full of water? If there were no interstices in the water, but the sun's rays had forcibly to part the water, full vessels would overflow. But this is not seen to occur. Here is another proof. If the rays forcibly parted the water they would all reach the bottom, instead of some being reflected and some reaching the bottom. What actually happens is that the rays that hit particles of water are reflected, those that find vacuums or encounter only a few particles of water get to the bottom.' Further proof of the porosity of water is found in the fact that if wine be poured into water it visibly disperses itself throughout the whole body of the water. A similar conclusion is drawn from the interpenetration of light by light. 'When more lamps are lighted the whole place shares in the increased illumination, since the rays of light are able to propagate themselves through one another.' Of course there are innumerable weaknesses in these demonstrations, but everywhere we are in the presence of a man who, where physical facts are in question, prefers a demonstration to an argument. We find further confirmation of Strato's habit of appealing to facts in a passage from another

39

writer, Simplicius (659, 22). He tells us that Strato, confronted with the endless debate as to whether change of position is possible without the supposition of a continuous vacuum, settled the matter by a simple demonstration. He put a stone into a closed vessel full of water, inverted the vessel, and showed that the stone changed its place.

Not only was he fertile in devising experiments, but he made also the most penetrating applications of his principles in many new fields. Here for example, in a few sentences from an anonymous treatise which has come down to us in the Aristotelian corpus – sentences now confidently claimed for his – we find him laying the foundation of a correct theory of sound. 'All sounds, vocal or otherwise, arise from bodies falling on bodies or air falling on bodies. The propagation of sound is not due to the air taking on a shape, as some suppose, but to its being an elastic medium which contracts and expands in accordance with the impulse imparted to it ... For when the impact of the breath strikes the air, the air is violently moved and imparts the same motion to the air next to it with the result that the same sound is carried out in every direction as far as the movement of the air extends.'

These examples are enough to show that Strato had fully established the experimental method and that he had given it a wonderfully wide application. It is important for us also to realize the independence of mind that he displayed in doing so. It has already been said that Theophrastus had thrown overboard the Aristotelian conception of matter. Strato is prepared to go much further. He throws overboard also Aristotle's doctrine of weight. Aristotle had taught that two of the elements, Earth and Water, have a natural tendency to move downwards, which he called gravity, while the other two, Air and Fire, have a natural tendency to move upwards, which he called levity. That is to say, Aristotle attempted to relate his doctrine of weight to a theory of 'natural place', each element in the universe having a place to which it naturally tended. For this Strato substituted the view of Democritus that weight is motion towards the centre, that all the elements have gravity and none levity, but that the lighter rest on the heavier, and that mass depends on the greater or less amount of matter in a given volume. But it must not be supposed from this that Strato had abjured Aristotle only to swear allegiance to Democritus and his atoms. Not so. For though he accepts from Democritus the idea of void within bodies he rejects the idea of an external continuous void. Though he believes that matter consists of minute invisible particles he rejects the idea that all the qualities of things depend on the size, shape and position of the atoms, as we have just seen, for instance in his theory of sound. There is evidence also that he sought to escape from the mechanistic outlook of Democritus.

At this point it becomes appropriate to consider what the general world-view of this great experimentalist was. It is clear that with him all anthropomorphic and teleological ideas have been finally cast aside. Cicero tells us (*On the Nature of the Gods*, I, 13, 35) that 'Strato the physicist was of opinion that all divine power resides in nature, and that nature, which is a power without shape or capacity to feel, contains in itself all the causes of coming to be, of growth, and of decay.' In another passage (*Academics*, II, 38, 121) which seems to reflect Strato's lively controversial style, Cicero records his views at slightly greater length. 'Strato of Lampsacus gives god a dispensation from his arduous task, opining that if the priests of the gods get holidays it is only fair that the gods should have them too. He says he does not use the help of the gods to make the world. Everything that exists, he says, is the work of nature, but adds that he does not mean that in the sense of the great man who said that all things are concretions of atoms, rough and smooth, hooked and barbed, with an admixture of void. These views he called the dreams of Democritus who could not prove them but only desired them. He himself goes through the parts of the universe one by one and proves that whatever exists or comes to be has been made or is made by purely natural forces and movements.' The standpoint of Strato is clear. His wish is to identify the divine with nature and at the same time to regard the whole of nature as the legitimate field of scientific enquiry. It is a bold effort to eliminate the idea of the supernatural, but it is not the first time we have met it in our study of the history of Greek thought. The view was characteristic also of some of the Hippocratic doctors (see Vol. I, pp. 73 and 74).

As was usual with Strato, who, unlike Theophrastus, does not seem to have wished to hesitate between two opinions, he worked his principles out to their logical conclusion in every branch of science. We shall conclude our account of him by an indication of his views on the nature of man and his place in the scheme of things.

Psychology already had a long and honourable history among the Greeks in the two hundred years which separate Alcmaeon from Aristotle. But Strato was able here also to register a remarkable advance. When faced with the old debate as to whether all knowledge originates in experience or whether, as Plato taught, true knowledge is independent of experience, being a possession of the soul before it is housed in the mortal body, Strato could not hesitate. He must place its source in experience. He accepted, of course, the now familiar distinction between the sense-organs and the mind. His originality, and the signal advance he made over the brilliant psychological work of Aristotle, lay in the way in which he conceived the relation between the senses and the mind. He was, with the possible exception of Diogenes of Apollonia, the first Greek to say clearly that it is not in the sense-organ but in the mind that an objective stimulus is transformed into a sensation. This is a piece of analysis of truly fundamental importance.

The recognition of the activity of the mind in sensation enables Strato to assert firmly the idea of the unity of the soul. With him both perception and thought become activities of the same soul. This not only rules out the Platonic notion of the soul as a strange immaterial visitant temporarily lodged in its house of clay. It cuts the ground also from under Aristotle's attempt to teach the mortality of the soul (*psyche*) and the immortality of the intellect (*nous*). Strato's doctrine has the further effect of permitting the recognition of the kinship of man with the animals. If we think and perceive with the same organ, the mind, it follows that the animals, who have sense-organs and perceive, have also in some degree mind. It was the opinion of Strato that every living thing can be in some degree the bearer of mind. Plutarch (961 *b*) preserves his opinion on this point. 'It follows', Strato argued, 'that everything that has perception has also intelligence, if it is by the exercise of intelligence that nature makes us able to perceive.' Rodier, the first of the moderns to make a systematic investigation into the physical opinions of Strato, was of the opinion that the influence of the philosopher Epicurus upon him was great. This may very well be true. In any case there is no room for doubt that Strato held the view of the Epicureans, the best anthropologists of the ancient world, that man is a superior kind of animal, not the view that animals are a degenerate kind of man.

For the small size of our volume we have given rather full accounts of the work of Theophrastus and Strato. Lest, however, the impression should be created that only the heads of the institution did any work, we shall include mention of three other scientific works produced by the Lyceum, one on chemistry, one on mechanics, one on music. The first two are anonymous, the third is by Aristoxenus.

CHEMISTRY

What I have called the work on chemistry has come down to us as Book IV of the *Meteorology* of Aristotle. Ross describes the contents of the whole treatise in these terms : 'Its subject (that is, of Books I–III) is in the main weather phenomena such as wind and rain, thunder and lightning, together with certain astronomical phenomena (such as comets and the milky way) which Aristotle wrongly believed to be not astronomical but meteorological. But the fourth book deals with quite a different set of facts – with composite bodies such as metals, and their sensible qualities.' This fourth book has been generally regarded as not by Aristotle, it is so intimately concerned with a multiplicity of practical activities connected with the crafts. If it should ever be accepted as the work of Aristotle I should have to modify the assertion I made in my first volume that 'the desire to *act* upon matter never troubled Aristotle'. For this treatise, the purpose of which is (I again quote Ross) 'to consider in detail the operation of the active qualities heat and cold and the modifications of the passive qualities dryness and fluidity'', contains, among much else of interest, an extraordinary programme of research into the nature of various substances with a view to classifying them in accordance with their ability or inability to be acted upon. I translate a short passage : 'Let us begin by enumerating those qualities expressing the aptitude or inaptitude of a thing to be affected in a certain way. They are as follows : to be apt or inapt to solidify, melt, be softened by heat, be softened by water, bend, break, be comminuted, impressed, moulded, squeezed, to be tractile, malleable, fissile, be cut, be viscous or friable, compressible or incompressible, combustible or incombustible, apt or inapt to give off fumes.' The programme of experiments here envisaged is worthy of Francis Bacon. It has been pointed out to me[5] that in two undoubtedly genuine works (*Parts of Animals*, 649*a* and *Generation of Animals*, 784*b*) Aristotle accepts the conclusions established in *Meteorology*, IV, as the considered statement of his own views. It would follow from this that such chemical researches as are here described – which are of the same kind as those in Theophrastus's work *On Fire* – were already in vogue in the Lyceum in Aristotle's day.

MECHANICS

The book on Mechanics is thought by Ross to belong to the early Peripatetic school, 'perhaps to Strato or one of his pupils'. Its best translator, Professor E. S. Forster, remarks of it : 'Whilst the scientific standpoint is certainly Peripatetic, the writer's interest in the practical applications of the problems involved is quite un-Aristotelian.' But we have already seen reason to doubt the validity of this argument. Its opening general statement, before it gets down to particular problems, is as follows : 'Things may occur either in accordance with nature or contrary to nature. Events in the former class excite our wonder when we do not know their cause. What excites our wonder in the second class is the ingenuity with which man pursues his advantage. Nature does many things in a way opposite to what we require. This results from the fact that the action of nature is uniform and simple, while human requirements are various and changing. When we require an effect contrary to nature, we are in difficulties

5. By Mr. David Eichholz of Bristol University.

and at a loss and require technical skill. The skilled invention which gets us out of our difficulty we call a device or a mechanism. It was the poet Antiphon who wrote :

> By skill victorious nature we defeat,

and he was right. Examples of what he meant are where smaller things control greater, or where small forces move great weights, or in general everything we include under the term mechanical problem. Mechanical problems are neither identical with physical problems nor entirely distinct from them. They rest upon a combination of mathematical and physical theory. The general principle is disclosed by mathematics, the application belongs to physics.'

There follows a brilliant attempt to bring a great range of human activities within the scope of mathematical explanation. These activities are concerned with the lever, the balance, the position of rowers in a boat, the steering-oar, arrangement of sails, the varieties of circular movement in the cart-wheel, the pulley and the potter's wheel, the sling, the strengths of varying lengths of wood, the wedge, the steelyard, the advantage of the forceps over the bare hand in the extraction of teeth, cracking nuts, the proper proportions in the construction of beds, the transport of long timbers, swing-beams at wells, the motion of wagons (involving the problem of inertia). Two questions are touched on that concern natural rather than human agency – the shaping of pebbles on a beach and the eddies in water. The whole constitutes an admirable essay in applied mathematics. Some of the main principles of statics are expounded with surprising success, namely the law of virtual velocities, the parallelogram of forces, the law of inertia.

Nothing is more astonishing in the genius of the age we have under discussion than the capacity of the great founders of the sciences to bring order out of chaos by delimiting the true field of particular branches of knowledge. Aristotle himself had done this with superb mastery, his comprehensive grasp of the whole field of human knowledge being matched by his capacity to draw firm boundaries between the various parts. The conception was formed of an organic body of scientific knowledge, covering the whole field of human experience, in which the separate parts which made up the whole should be clearly separated from one another yet seen in their mutual relations. With this master plan before them his disciples continued his work, now reconsidering the basic principles of the whole structure (as when Theophrastus raised the whole problem of the validity of the teleological principle), now defining the limits of the particular sciences more clearly (as when Theophrastus, by his analysis of the nature of the parts of animals and plants, separated the sciences of zoology and botany). So too we have seen Strato reconstituting two branches of science—the theory of the fundamental structure of matter and the theory of the nature of the soul. We have seen two other members of the school, whose names are uncertain – an indication of the teamwork which was practised there – constituting branches of chemistry and of applied mathematics. We have now to turn to another great man, Aristoxenus, who brought order into the interpretation of one of the major branches of art, namely music.

MUSIC

Aristoxenus, a contemporary of Theophrastus, was born at Tarentum, an ancient seat of varied culture. He was the son of a distinguished musician, Spintharus, who had travelled much and been in contact with many of the great men of the day. It was almost inevitable that the scion of this powerful and intellectual family should be enrolled sooner or later at the Lyceum. Aristoxenus, in fact, not only became a Peripatetic and a pupil of Aristotle, he held such a position in the school that he entertained hopes of succeeding his master. We cannot say that Aristoxenus would have made a better head than Theophrastus. It is worth recording, however, that besides his work on musical theory he wrote philosophy and biography.

The special achievement of this man, with his wide, practical knowledge of music and his deep philosophical training, was eminently characteristic of the school to which he belonged. It consisted in the accurate determination of the scope of musical science and the establishment of a truer conception of the real nature of music itself. Up to the time of Aristoxenus music in Greece had been in the position of an Art, a Techne. There were, of course, schools of musical art. There was conscious preference of one style of composition to another. There were musical competitions in abundance, where a wide public learned an exquisite discrimination in the style and talents of various performers. Makers of instruments were famous for their skill. All the habits formed by these preferences were transmitted by instruction from generation to generation of craftsmen, composers and executants. But nowhere in all this do we perceive any apprehension of the basic principles of a science of music as such.

How were such principles to be come by? The only school that had seriously concerned itself with the endeavour to establish a science of music was the Pythagorean. But, though the Pythagoreans spoke of music, they had not risen above the level of acoustics. They reduced sound to air vibrations. Where the ear hears high and low, they detected mathematical relations which appeal to the intellect. These were remarkable scientific achievements, but they do not constitute a science of *music*. The mere principles of sound do not supply any basis for the criticism or appreciation of music. Aristoxenus, who was of course aware of what the Pythagoreans had done, understood that they had not yet got to the point. He saw that true musical science must accept, as elements requiring no further explanation, such conceptions as voice, interval, high, low, concord, discord. Its task must be to reduce the more complex phenomena of music to these simple forms and to ascertain the general laws of their connection.

Here was a clear definition of the scope of musical science which brought with it a deeper conception of music itself. The essence of music lies in the dynamical relations of sounds to one another, not in the physical and mathematical antecedents of sounds. Aristoxenus had now found a definition of music which made possible the understanding of the essential nature of a musical composition as a system of sounds, in which no sound has a meaning by itself but in which every sound acquires a meaning by virtue of its relation to all the rest. Here is a key sentence : 'Our method rests in the last resort on an appeal to the two faculties of hearing and intellect; by the former we judge the magnitudes of the intervals, by the latter we contemplate the functions of the notes.'

This achievement of Aristoxenus finds its nearest parallel in the *Poetics* of Aristotle where for the first time science had been successfully applied to the analysis of a great branch of art. With the *Poetics* of Aristotle and the *Harmonics* of Aristoxenus the basis had been laid for an intelligent and conscious criticism of the nature and function of art. The human spirit had made immense gains in its consciousness of itself.

With this we end our recital of the scientific achievement of the Lyceum. It only remains to admit that at the death of

Strato the popularity of the institution was in full decline. Under the eloquent Theophrastus, who maintained all the manifold activities, cultural and scientific, which had characterized the work of the school under its founder, we are told (Diogenes Laertius, V, 37) that as many as two thousand students were in the habit of attending the lectures. These days were no more. The education most required and desired by the citizen was a knowledge of men and affairs, and the gift of speech. Something plausible to say and the ability to say it with effect was the supreme necessity for a public man. Strato, in shifting the main emphasis of the institution onto scientific research, failed to meet the popular demand, and the numbers of students fell. His choice of a successor fell upon Lyco, a man who had no capacity as a scientist but was distinguished for his cultural attainments. The appointment was made by Strato in his will, the text of which has been preserved for us. It suggests that the school was in difficulties. 'I leave the school to Lyco, since the others are either too old or too busy.' This is a back-handed compliment. 'It would be well if the others would co-operate with him.' Obviously there is dissension. 'I bequeath to him all my books, *except those of which I am the author.*' Does this mean that Lyco had no use for them? The facts, at least, are that Lyco shifted the weight of interest from natural philosophy to ethics and rhetoric and sought to revive the more popular features of the school, particularly the afternoon lectures. We may perhaps draw the conclusion that a programme of physical research, with a strong bias towards the practical applications of science, such as we find in Theophrastus *On Fire,* in Strato *On the Vacuum,* in *Meteorology,* IV, and *On Mechanical Problems,* had become functionless in a city such as Athens, which had lost the leadership in Greek affairs and was materially in a state of decay.

The Lyceum had always owed much to Macedonian patronage. Aristotle was a Macedonian. His father had been physician at the court of Philip, the Macedonian king. Aristotle had been tutor to Philip's son, Alexander the Great. The Lyceum was, in a very definite sense, a centre of Macedonian influence in Athens. Strato, before he had been called to Athens to be made head of the school, had been appointed by the founder of the new Macedonian dynasty in Egypt to be tutor to his son. We have evidence that the career of the Lyceum had not always been untroubled by the shifts and changes of Athenian politics. There was arising in Egypt a new Macedonian power with aspirations to be the strongest power in the Mediterranean world. The Ptolemies have left the clearest proof that they were acutely aware of the service that science could be made to render to government. There is therefore nothing to be surprised at in the fact that they exerted their powerful influence to transfer from Athens to Alexandria every activity of the Lyceum which they thought could be of use to them. The scientific future lay, not with Lyco and his inconspicuous successors in Athens, but with the Museum of Alexandria and the brilliant band of scholars and scientists gathered and maintained there by the magic of Ptolemaic gold.

BIBLIOGRAPHICAL NOTE

The articles in Pauly-Wissowa, *Real-Encyclopädie*, on Peripatos (by K. O. Brink), on Theophrastus (by O. Regenbogen), on Strato (by Capelle) give a comprehensive and up-to-date review of the history of the Lyceum after Aristotle. For the opportunity to consult the first two I am indebted to Dr. Brink. Brunet et Mieli, *Histoire des Sciences : Antiquité* are valuable for the whole period, but where they follow Senn's lead on Theophrastus do not carry conviction against the criticism of Regenbogen. The *Metaphysics* of Theophrastus was edited with translation by Ross and Forbes, Oxford, 1929. *Meteorology*, IV, and *Mechanics* will be found in the *Works of Aristotle translated into English*, Oxford. In the Loeb Library will be found a translation by Sir Arthur Hort of *The Enquiry into Plants* (i.e. *The History of Plants*) of Theophrastus.

CHAPTER TWO

History and organization of the Museum – Planned religion and planned science – Engineers – Doctors – Mathematicians – Astronomers – Geographers – Astronomy Again – The organization of learning – Grammar

★

HISTORY AND ORGANIZATION OF THE MUSEUM

THERE was a sort of American opulence about the new centre of learning in the Egyptian capital. Formally the Museum was, what its name implies, a Temple of the Muses, and its head was a high priest. But its real purpose was to be a research institute which also went in for teaching. In both these respects it was modelled on the Lyceum, but on a vastly larger scale. Its library, which incorporated that of Aristotle, had about half a million rolls, and the direction of research and teaching seems to have lain with the librarian. There were about a hundred professors whose salaries were provided by the king. There were rooms for research, for lectures and for study. The Lyceum had studied astronomy, biology and botany. For the prosecution of these studies the Museum supplied an observatory, a zoo, a botanical garden. There were also dissecting rooms. Such opportunities for research and scholarship had never existed before. Good use was made of them.

It is not possible to give an exact date for the foundation of the Museum. Alexander had conquered Egypt in 332 B.C. His general Ptolemy, son of Lagus, who had been appointed satrap, took control when Alexander died in 323. When he proclaimed himself king in 305 he assumed the cognomen Soter (Saviour). Two years before his death he had been succeeded by his son Philadelphus, whose tutor Strato had been. Philadelphus reigned from 285 to 247. It was under these first two Ptolemies that the Museum took shape. It had in all a history of some six hundred years, but the first couple of centuries, from Euclid to Hipparchus, are the all-important ones. Then the various branches of ancient science were systematized. Then was established the fashion and the art of writing those orderly treatises, expounding a subject from its first principles to its latest conclusions, which entitled this period to be called the Age of the Text-book. It marks a real stage in human progress.

The Macedonian monarchs who founded and maintained the Museum were the successors of a ruling family which had long shown that it understood the connection between science and government. Philip and Alexander owed their military success largely to engineers. They did not allow themselves to be stopped by walls. Alexander showed that he knew also how to build and organize. The Ptolemies, in charge of Egypt, would have been neglecting an obvious duty if they had not made provision for the training of engineers, doctors, astronomers, mathematicians, geographers. In a more haphazard way the chief Greek city-states had long provided such men for their more limited needs. Vast territories were now to be organized and scientists and technicians had to be secured in a more systematic way. The fame of the Athenian schools had also resulted in the growth of a new pride in every branch of literary culture.

The new conditions in Egypt, however, provided a novel environment for Greek science and culture, which were traditionally national and local. The Academy and the Lyceum were personal ventures. But Alexandria was the Greek capital of a great Egyptian territory and the State was behind the organization of the Museum. Greek science was required to take root in a new soil and play an altered role. The cosmopolitan character of the huge city was a new

54

thing. The court and the army were Greek, and for the capital he required the first Ptolemy relied on Greek business men. These constituted the ruling class. In the cities there was an international proletariat, mainly Greek, consisting of petty traders, artisans and the like. Of the city-dwellers the Jews, after the Greeks, were culturally and socially the most important. The population of the country at large was Egyptian, and, though there is evidence that some Greeks inter-married with Egyptians, the mass of the natives remained untouched by the advent of a Macedonian government and its imported Greek culture.

For the wealthy ruling-class Greek the familiar master-slave relation was still the dominant feature in the structure of society and in the structure of his thought. Life was still inconceivable without the personal attendance of the chattel slave. But Egyptian, Jewish and other cultures now made a direct impact upon his own, and the Ptolemies had succeeded to the problems of government of the Pharaohs, with the additional complication of being foreigners. Various sources recently explored throw some light on the composition of Egyptian society. At the base of the social pyramid was a depressed and numerous population, performing among other exacting functions one that was demanded by the very nature of the soil. Egypt is called the gift of the Nile. But without the incessant toil of myriads of hands, maintained generation after generation, the gift would have been a barren one. The Nile does not irrigate the land of Egypt without human aid. There was an enormous network of irrigation canals, including long underground passages giving access to subterranean springs, to be kept in order. To be born into the class of those who did this work was re-garded as a hopeless doom. The 'toil-worn water-leaders, burdened water-carriers, burrowers into underground passages, earning a miserly wage which gave them no prospect

of ever owning anything of their own as a fruit of their toil'
were held by the ancient astrologers to have been born under
a disastrous conjunction of planetary influences. Along with
them we learn of the workers in other humble trades – the
bakers, for instance, whose affliction, then as in all later ages,
was the necessity of working by night in order that others
might eat by day ; the porters, with burdens on their backs
like dumb beasts ; the quarrymen and those who carried
away the cut stones, not to speak of the children who shifted
the rubble ; the divers for sponges and the bath attendants
who 'died in early youth', since theirs were dangerous trades.
According to the latest evidence these poor Egyptians were
wage earners, not slaves. Their lot was none the less wretched.
It was the traditional old poverty-stricken Egypt which the
Ptolemies had undertaken to govern, and needless to say
their efforts were not directed to transforming their conditions of life. The inventive genius of the scientists and
mechanists called into existence by the Museum could not,
at this date in the world's history, be applied in the Russian
manner to the relief of mass misery. On the contrary, except
for certain necessities of the State (chiefly the provision of
engines of war) and certain amenities of the rich (like
garden-fountains) science tended more and more to retreat
from its function as man's weapon in the fight against nature
and confine itself to its function of being a mental discipline
for the contemplative. For the relief of the needs of the poor
government continued to cater by religion.

PLANNED RELIGION AND PLANNED SCIENCE

Before the advent of the Ptolemies the Egyptians had not
lacked this commodity. But with the establishment of a
Greek government in an Egyptian population new problems
had arisen. A god pointed the way to a solution. The first

Ptolemy learned in a vision of the night that a new worship was required and was advised to fetch a statue of Pluto from a temple of Jupiter in Sinope to help furnish a centre for the new cult. The proper execution of this divine intimation required care and elaboration. A combination of native Egyptian with imported Greek theology proved equal to the task. The Egyptian priest Manetho and the Greek priest Timotheus worked out the attributes of the new god and decided on his name. He was to be called Serapis. His temple, the Serapeum, was one of the most sumptuous monuments of the ancient world. A statue by the sculptor Bryaxis, of the school of Scopas in the middle of the fourth century, was selected for the cult image. The liturgical language was Greek. The new cult, says Loisy,[1] was 'a carefully thought out adaptation of the religion of Egypt to the spirit and habits of the Greeks'.

The new god showed immediate signs of vitality. Among his other attributes he was a god of healing and he performed miracles from the first. The Athenian philosopher, Demetrius of Phalerum, a member of the Peripatetic school and a pupil of Theophrastus, being cured by him of blindness, composed paeans in his honour which were still being sung centuries later. Such blessings could not be confined to the capital. By the second century A.D. there were forty-two Serapeums in Egypt. But the god had still wider ambitions. His worship very early spread to Cyprus, Sicily, Antioch, Athens. Later it reached the coasts of Syria, Asia Minor and Greece, the islands of the Aegean, the Hellespont and Thrace. At Delos, the centre also of the slave trade, the Roman merchants were rivals, in their devotion to the god, of the Greek aristocrats who maintained the cult. The cult lasted till the end of paganism and beyond it. It penetrated Italy, where it is

1. *Les Mystères Païens et le Mystère Chrétien*, 1930.

attested at Puteoli before the end of the second century B.C. About the same time it reached Pompeii. The senate tried to arrest its spread among the populace at Rome, choosing itself to introduce new religions rather than to tolerate those introduced by the people. But authority in the end gave way. It was probably in A.D. 38 that the emperor Caligula built his great temple to Isis (who shared the worship of Serapis) in the Campus Martius.

Cumont[2] observes that the art and literature of Greece were put at the service of the new religion created by Ptolemy. He omits to mention science. But science had also its mite to contribute. For science never succeeds in remaining neutral, in remaining pure. When it lost its ambition to transform the material life of man by being applied to industry it quickly acquired fresh applications. It became the handmaid of religion and was applied to the production of miracles in the Serapeums and other temples of Egypt. Strato had proudly averred that he did not need the help of the gods to make a world. The gods did not disdain the help of Strato to run this one. Hero of Alexandria, who has preserved the record of Strato's work on pneumatics, explains to us how this and other branches of science will be found useful 'not only in providing the most fundamental requisites of civilized life but also in producing bewilderment and awe'. The bewilderment and awe refer to the effects of the temple miracles.

Most of the miracles described by Hero depend on one or other of two principles – the siphon and the expansive power of heated air. They were applications of the pneumatics of Strato. The principle of the siphon was applied in a great variety of ingenious ways to counterfeit the turning of water into wine. Water poured in at one end in a system of siphons

2. *Religions Orientales dans le Paganisme Romain*, 1929.

resulted in wine coming out at the other. The expansive power of hot air produced supernatural movements. An air chamber in an altar was connected with a shrine of the deity above. When the offering was burned on the altar the expanding air opened the door of the shrine, propelled the deity forward and caused him to salute the worshipper. This principle had many other applications. From other sources we learn of the religious applications of the principles of another Alexandrian science, optics, to the production of apparitions. To the conscience of the age these scientific aids to devotion hardly differed in principle from the use of improved lighting effects or the introduction of organ music, which also were achievements of this age. They were intended to create a pious public, to make religion attractive and impressive, and seem to have done so.

We have, for instance, an account by the accomplished poet Claudian of an unusual type of temple miracle which conveys also the impression of the ceremonial which attended the routine performance of the pious fraud. The natural force employed in this instance was that of the magnet. The scene was a joint temple of Mars and Venus. The divine actors were a Mars made of polished iron and a loadstone Venus. Preparations were made for the marriage of the two. Myrtle wreaths adorned the portals of the marriage chamber. The couch was heaped with roses, the coverlets were of purple. The priest went through the marriage service. The choir entered singing, preceded by the nuptial torch. There were lights, music, colour, odours and ritual. It is to be presumed that the congregation responded to these effects. Then came the miracle. The iron figure of Mars was brought within the ambit of attraction of the loadstone Venus. 'Without quitting her station, the goddess by her potent charm draws the god into her arms. She clasps him to her bosom with amorous breath', says the poet, embroidering his theme.[3] The date of this poem is about A.D. 400. The scientific production of miracles covers the whole period of the rise and fall of Alexandrian science. It is not without a bearing on it. When science began to flourish again in the modern world it had another purpose than to deceive.

THE ENGINEER

So it had in antiquity also, but in a strangely limited degree. A quotation from Brunet and Mieli will give us a preliminary view of the character of Alexandrian science, to the study of which we must now turn. 'It is certain', they write, 'that the ancient engineers in general, not only those of Alexandria, tried only exceptionally to apply their machines to useful results. It did not occur to them, for instance, to apply the force of water, of compressed air, or of steam, as a source of power in their trades or to obtain results analogous to those which the development of modern civilization has revealed. One might even suppose that with the knowledge that they had, and availing themselves of the mechanisms they thought out for their toys, the ancient engineers might have arrived at applications analogous to those that make the glory of the eighteenth century. However, in recording their failure, sufficiently curious in itself for the modern mind, one must of course recognize that the attention of the technicians of Antiquity was not exclusively applied to toys. Some truly useful machines were constructed, like pumps for raising water or putting out fires. The ingenuity of the Alexandrians exercised itself above all in the perfecting of a great number of instruments of precision, very delicate in

3. C. E. N. Bromehead (*Geology in Embryo*, Proceedings of the Geologists' Association, Vol. LVI, Part 2, 1945, p. 115), while not denying that a large piece of magnetite might attract a small statuette, suspects the use of fine cords invisible in a dim religious light.

construction, and indispensable even for the progress of science. Such were their astronomical instruments and their water-clocks.'

It is now generally agreed that the founder of the Alexandrian school of mechanists was Ctesibius. Ctesibius, whose lifetime fell within the reigns of the second and third Ptolemies, that is between 285 and 222, was the son of an Alexandrian barber. An early achievement of his was to facilitate the raising and lowering of a mirror in the barber's shop by balancing it with a lump of lead. Suspended on a cord, this ran up and down in a pipe concealed behind a beam. Where there is mother wit one thing soon leads to another. The fact that when the lead fell rapidly down the pipe it forced the air out with a squeak suggested to the ingenious barber's son the invention of a mechanical musical instrument. This, when finally perfected, was the famous water-organ, an instrument in whose tones Cicero some two hundred years later tells us he found great delight. The power was supplied by a column of water supported on a cushion of air. The air passed through a valve into a horizontal cylinder connected with a series of vertical organ pipes into which the air could be allowed to enter through valves controlled by jacks.

The introduction of mechanical music is no mean contribution to civilization. But the hydraulis was not the only achievement of Ctesibius. Equally famous were his water-clocks. The description which follows is taken from Vitruvius (IX, viii, 4 and 5). It will be intelligible to one who studies the accompanying illustration. 'For the water-inlet he used a hole bored in a piece of gold or in a gem, finding that these neither wear nor get blocked. This secured an even flow. The water as it rose floated an inverted bowl, technically known as the cork or drum. This connected with a bar and a revolving drum. Both bar and drum had teeth at regular

intervals fitting into one another. By this means the recti-
linear motion of the rising cork was transformed into a
series of small measured circular movements. By an elaboration of this device through a number of rods and cogs he
caused a variety of movements. The little figure which
pointed to the hour moved. The cylinder of the clock re-
volved. Stones or eggs were dropped. Trumpets were
sounded, and there were other incidental effects.' The dis-
cerning reader will notice here some knowledge of materials
as well as of mechanical principles. It should be observed
that the construction of these clocks was unnecessarily complicated by the antique fashion of hours which varied in
length according to the seasons of the year. Day and night,
darkness and light, were divided into twelve intervals. The
hours of day were long in summer and short in winter.
Ctesibius contrived clocks which conformed to this inconvenient convention, just as we adapt instruments and tables
to our primitive metrical system.

Apart from the water-organ and the water-clock Ctesibius
invented pieces of artillery working by compressed air and
a double-action pump for raising water which was utilized
in fire-engines. Mechanical difficulties of construction made
the former ineffective. The fire-engine, equally remarkable
theoretically, was more of a practical success and is generally
regarded as his masterpiece.

Ctesibius is known to us only by reports of his chief inventions. His younger contemporary, Philo of Byzantium,
has had the good fortune to be represented by still surviving
fragments of his comprehensive treatise on mechanics. A
study of the contents of its nine books helps us to understand the social function of science at this time. So far as we
can judge, it dealt with Principles and Applications of the
Lever, Construction of Harbours, Ballistics or Artillery,
Pneumatics or Machines using Compressed Air, the Con-

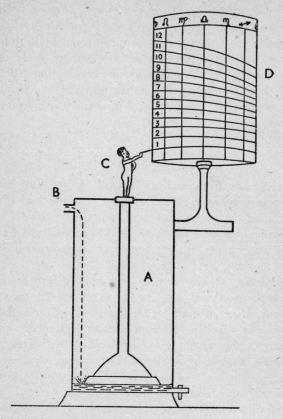

WATERCLOCK OF CTESIBIUS

A – container with float.

B – hole cut in gold or precious stone, through which water enters.

C – figure which rises with float and points to the hours.

D – drum which revolves once a year, showing the hours varying in length according to the seasons. The vertical lines indicate the months.

struction of Automata, Defence of Towns, Siege of Towns, and probably some other aspects of war. Apparently the main application of mechanics was to war. The attention to harbours illustrates the more constructive activity of the age. The automata and the pneumatic machines without doubt found their main application to the provision of amenities and miracles. The application of mechanics to industry is lacking.

THE DOCTOR

Let us turn now from mechanics to medicine. We have made some acquaintance with the work of Ctesibius and Philo who carried on the work of the Lyceum in mechanics and pneumatics. Let us leave them for Herophilus and Erasistratus who carried on the tradition of the Lyceum in biological research.

Herophilus, who came from Chalcedon in Bithynia and flourished about 300 B.C., wrote a general treatise *On Anatomy*, a special study *Of the Eyes*, and a handbook for midwives in which he gives an elementary account of the anatomy of the womb. The handbook for midwives is a refreshing example of that humanitarian zeal which again and again shines out of the pages of the history of Greek medicine. It may also be regarded as the repayment by the scientist of a debt due to the craftswoman. It is a commonplace that in his vast collection of information on biological subjects Aristotle owed a debt to fisherfolk and stockbreeders. His debt to the midwife's profession is less well known and worth quoting. In his *History of Animals* (VII, 10) we find the following passage : 'The cutting of the navel-string is the duty of the midwife and requires an alert intelligence. In a difficult labour everything depends on her skill. She must have presence of mind to deal with emergencies and to manage the tying of the string. If the afterbirth comes away with the child, the navel-string is separated from the afterbirth by a knot and is severed above the knot. Where it is tied it grows together and the continuity is broken. But if the fastening comes undone the blood flows out and the child dies. If, on the other hand, the afterbirth does not come away at once, then the navel-string is tied and severed after the birth of the child while the afterbirth is still inside. It often happens that the child seems to be stillborn, if it is a weak child, and the blood flows out into the cord and the neighbouring parts. Experienced midwives then press the blood back out of the cord, when the child, as if it had been previously drained of blood, revives. As has been said already, children like other animals come out head first, and children have their arms stretched by their sides. Immediately on being born they cry and move their hands to their mouth. Some children evacuate immediately, some after a little time, all within a day. The evacuation, which is called the meconium, is more copious than the normal evacuation of a child.' The reference to the blood flowing into the cord and causing danger of stillbirth is wrong. It seems to be a misinterpretation of *asphyxia neonatorum*. But there is no doubt, in view of the fullness and accuracy of his remarks, that Aristotle had gone to the midwives for his facts. Herophilus keeps alive the contact between biological research and midwifery.

Of the contributions Herophilus made to anatomy the most fundamental was his investigation of the seat of the intelligence. In the fifth century Alcmaeon had located it correctly in the brain. A century later Aristotle, for ten excellent, but as it proved mistaken, reasons transferred it to the heart. Herophilus returned to the view of Alcmaeon on the basis of a diligent dissection of the nervous system and the brain. Anatomists before him had made some progress in tracing the nerves of the special senses. He was the first to get a general picture of the nervous system and to effect the distinction of the motor from the sensory nerves. The nomenclature of the parts of the brain still bears many traces of his work.

His younger contemporary, Erasistratus of Chios, partly carried on his work, partly struck out a line of his own. Singer tells us that the observations of Herophilus on the lacteals were extended by Erasistratus to a point beyond which no advance was made before Gasparo Aselli (1581–1626). But the work of Erasistratus for the most part lay in a new field. If Herophilus is to be called the founder of anatomy, then Erasistratus is the founder of physiology. His work, though he did not come to the correct conclusion, has a tremendous bearing on the question of the circulation of the blood. His success in advancing the knowledge of the heart is proved by his having observed the semi-lunar valves, the tricuspid and the bicuspid valves. He traced the subdivisions of the veins and arteries to the limits of vision and was confident that they must proceed beyond this. That with all this he should have failed to arrive at the theory of the circulation illustrates a fundamental difficulty in the progress of science.

In the infinite variety and complexity of the phenomena of nature the scientist is at a loss in which direction to turn unless he is looking for something. If he is looking for something that means he has a theory. If he has a theory he tends to see what supports it and to miss other significant facts. There is no way out of this difficulty except the patience and discipline which the long tradition of science can help to supply. In this situation an ardent and enthusiastic mind is more liable to error than one that is without these attractive qualities. There is no doubt of the zeal of Erasistratus for his ideal of science. It is the tradition, and the known facts confirm it, that Erasistratus and Strato profoundly influenced one another. Almost certainly the two men were personally acquainted. The similarity of their outlook was such that we have already felt justified in quoting from Erasistratus to illustrate the experimental technique of Strato. But they not only shared the experimental temper. They were working on the same problem in different fields. Erasistratus was a firm adherent of the theories of Strato on the vacuum and they provided the basis for his physiological system. This, in the end, was his undoing. Herophilus had had no doubt that the function of both veins and arteries was to carry blood. Erasistratus, fascinated by Strato's demonstration of the pull exercised on liquids by the void, found reason to conclude that the arteries are normally empty of blood. He knew, of course, that if you sever an artery in a living animal it spouts blood. But there was the contrary fact that in a dead animal the arteries are empty of blood but full of air – full of that air which, if rarefied, had the power, as Strato had shown, to suck up liquids. His observations of the minute subdivisions of veins and arteries had convinced Erasistratus that they were connected by capillary vessels. His knowledge of Stratonic pneumatics now revealed to him how he could reconcile the apparently contradictory facts that the arteries of a wounded animal spout blood while dissection of the dead animal shows them empty. He concluded that the arteries are normally filled with air, that when the artery is severed this air escapes, causing a vacuum, that the pull of this vacuum brings blood from the veins through the capillaries into the arteries, which then spouts out as it follows hard on the escaping air. This fatally ingenious explanation proved an obstacle for some time to a true view of the function of the arterial system. Four hundred and fifty years later we find Galen disproving the Erasistratan view by careful experiments in vivisection. Nearly fourteen hundred years after

Galen Vesalius repeated these experiments before his classes in Padua. These demonstrations of the presence of blood in the arteries became traditional and in another eighty years or so led Harvey, who had been a student at Padua, to his great discovery. The success of Harvey was not due to the fact that he had no false theories in his head. He had as many as Erasistratus but he paid no attention to them. The essential progress had consisted in the acquisition of the gift of patient observation.

MATHEMATICIANS

Mechanics and medicine are the two branches of Alexandrian science which exhibit most clearly the historical connection with the Lyceum. Mathematics, which in the opinion of many is the greatest achievement of Greek science, reflects rather the influence of the Academy. Not, of course, that the Lyceum was indifferent to this study. We have already mentioned the fact that one of Aristotle's pupils, Eudemus, wrote a history of mathematics. That work, written before 300 B.C., could not, even if it were extant, give us any information about the founder of Alexandrian geometry, Euclid, whose *Elements*, in thirteen books, is generally regarded as the greatest text-book in the whole history of science. But some seven hundred years after Eudemus a Neo-Platonic philosopher, Proclus (A.D. 410–485), engaged on the composition of a Commentary to Book I of Euclid, borrowed from Eudemus a sketch of the earlier history of geometry and proceeded against this background to sketch the special achievement of Euclid. This Commentary of Proclus is extant, and we shall summarize its opening pages. By this summary we hope to achieve three things – first, to bring out some facts about the earlier history of Greek mathematical science for which we have not yet found space; second, to define the qualities in

Euclid which have been so much admired both in ancient and modern times; and third, to give an example from a writer as late as Proclus of the care the Greeks devoted to the preservation of their great heritage even when they had lost the capacity to add to it. One of the chief glories of the Museum is that it established the tradition of scholarship, without which the creations of genius have little chance of survival.

Geometry, says Proclus, had its origin in Egypt, taking its rise from the perpetual necessity of resurveying the land after the Nile floods had removed the boundaries. This and every other science naturally have their origin in practical needs. Arithmetic similarly arose among the Phoenicians out of the requirements of commerce and contracts. Thales was the first to fetch the study out of Egypt to Greece. He had made progress in generalization which served as an example to his successors. But the man who transformed the study into a liberal education was Pythagoras. He endeavoured to base the science on fundamental principles, investigating his theorems by means of the pure intellect in abstraction from matter. He discovered the theory of proportionals and the construction of the cosmic figures. Distinguished men after him were Anaxagoras of Clazomenae, Oenopides of Chios, Hippocrates of Chios, who discovered the quadrature of the lune, and Theodorus of Cyrene. Hippocrates was the first to write *Elements*. Plato who came next gave a tremendous impetus to geometry by his enthusiasm for it. He filled his dialogues with references to mathematics and inspired all lovers of philosophy with respect for the subject. Contemporaries of his were Leodamas of Thasos, Archytas of Tarentum, and Theaetetus of Athens. A pupil of Leodamas, one Leon, wrote an improved *Elements*. Another to compose an excellently arranged *Elements* was Theudius. He, like Eudoxus of Cnidos, Amyclas of Heraclea, Menaechmus and his brother Dinostratus, Athenaeus of Cyzicus, Hermotimus of Colophon, and Philip of Medma, were all members of the Academy.

Those who have compiled histories, continues Proclus, carry the development of the science up to this point. Shortly after this came Euclid, the author of the *Elements*, who gave irrefutable proofs of the looser demonstrations of his predecessors. That he lived in the time of the first Ptolemy is proved by the fact that Archimedes refers to him. There is also his famous saying that *there is no royal road to geometry.* This was his reply when Ptolemy enquired whether there was no shorter path to geometry than by the elements. He was an adept in the Platonic philosophy and set as the end of the *Elements* the construction of the Platonic, or cosmic, figures. He wrote many other admirable scientific works, like his *Optics* and *Elements of Music*. But his great title to fame is his *Elements of Geometry*, which is notable not only for its order but for the selection of the material, for he did not put in all he could but only what could strictly be regarded as belonging to the elements. The *Elements* constitute an irrefutable and adequate guide to the scientific investigation of mathematical material. So much for the summary of Proclus.

English students of Greek geometry are in a fortunate position. Apart from excellent older works like Allman's *Greek Geometry* and Gow's *Short History of Greek Mathematics*, in 1921 came Sir Thomas Heath's now world-famous two-volume *History of Greek Mathematics*, which has been followed in 1939 and 1941 by Ivor Thomas's two volumes in the Loeb Library, *Greek Mathematical Works*. These cover the same ground as Heath's *History* but in a way that facilitates the study and enhances the value of the older work. While Heath offers a continuous history of his subject, Thomas has compiled a copious selection of material from

the extant Greek writers, with English translation opposite
and helpful introductions and notes. There is no royal road
to Greek geometry, but for English readers access to the
subject as a whole, or to particular parts of it, has been made
easy and reliable. For those who read Greek mention should
be made of Heath's annotated school edition of Euclid Book
I. Heath was surely not wrong in supposing that many
'would be really interested to see the actual language in
which the old Alexandrian taught the youth and pupils of
maturer age in his own day, and so to put themselves in the
place of their fellow-students of twenty-two centuries ago'.

With Euclid and his immediate successors, Archimedes of
Syracuse and Apollonius of Perga, Alexandrian mathematics
achieved such developments that they require a specialist to
understand and describe them. The present writer, at any
rate, has not the mathematical equipment to understand
Archimedes' extant works, *On the Sphere and the Cylinder,
On Conoids and Spheroids, On Spirals, On the Quadrature
of the Parabola*. The subject-matter of the little treatise called
The Sand-Reckoner is more accessible to lay apprehension.
The point of it is this. The Greeks used an alphabetic notation in their arithmetical calculations which made the hand-
ling of large numbers difficult. Where we use but ten
symbols and easily express the highest numbers by the significance we attach to their position, the Greeks used twenty-
seven alphabetical signs and did not exploit the advantages
of a positional notation. Their minds were thus haunted by
the idea that the expression of very large numbers would
demand the use of an immense number of symbols. Archimedes' little book, which is addressed to King Gelo of Syracuse, sets these fears at rest. He expounds a system he has
invented by means of which, if the whole universe were conceived to consist of grains of sand and if that number were
known, it could be simply and conveniently expressed. The

highest number he expresses would in our notation be represented by 1 followed by eighty thousand million million o's.

The title of Apollonius to fame rests on his *Conic Sections*. In a dedicatory letter to a friend he describes the scope of his work. The composition of the book, he says, was suggested to him by a geometer called Naucrates who made a stay with him in Alexandria, and he finished off the eight books as quickly as he could because Naucrates had to sail, which left insufficient time for revision. He is now publishing a revised edition and begs his friend not to be surprised if some of the propositions have got about in their earlier and less perfect form. The first four books offer an orderly exposition of the elements of conics, the last four deal with a number of miscellaneous problems. The chief topics of the first books are : (1) Methods of producing the three sections; (2) Properties of the diameters and axes of the sections; (3) Theorems useful for the syntheses of solid loci and for determining limits of possibility; (4) Investigation of the number of times the sections of cones can meet one another and the circumference of a circle. He is careful to indicate what is his own contribution to the general stock of knowledge of the subject.

Our other allusions to the geometry of the Greeks will be incidental to our account of their astronomy, where they found their principal application, but before we leave the subject one general observation is necessary. The extraordinary success of Euclid in exhibiting the whole of geometry as a logical deduction from a small number of definitions, postulates and common notions, set a standard of scientific truth which the Greeks attempted to apply not only in the field of pure mathematics but also in observational and experimental sciences like astronomy and mechanics. Here the results were not so satisfactory. The scientist tended to regard as science whatever could be included as deductions from a few self-evident principles in a logically constructed system. The readiness to question the fundamental assumptions in the light of fresh observations whether of natural phenomena or of controlled processes was discouraged by the passion for logical consistency. System-building tended to take the place of research, and what could not be made to fit into the system was left on one side. The strength and the weakness of this ideal will be apparent in what follows.

Archimedes (287–212) is very generally regarded not only as the greatest mathematician but as the greatest mechanist or engineer of antiquity. Some would claim for him also, more doubtfully, that after Strato he best understood the experimental method. We have spoken of his mathematical works. His engineering works include the construction of a planetarium, which Cicero says reproduced all the unequal and different movements of the heavenly bodies. He invented a screw for raising water which had application both to irrigation in Egypt and to raising water in mines. It is not certain how it worked, but recent information suggests that it involved exhausting labour for slaves. He moved great weights by a system of compound pulleys. The military engines he devised for the defence of Syracuse seem never to have been outdone in the ancient world. His devotion to experiment is proved by more than one passage. Most interesting, perhaps, is the account, given in the opening pages of the *Sandreckoner*, of his efforts to make a more accurate determination of the angle subtended at the eye by the sun's disk. His predecessor Aristarchus had given it as the seven hundred and twentieth part of the circle of the Zodiac, i.e., half a degree. To secure a more accurate estimate Archimedes observed the sun as soon as it came above the horizon, when alone it could be observed by the naked eye, by means of a carefully turned circular disk mounted at right angles on the end of a long rule. The distance of the disk from the eye could be altered. Archimedes took two kinds of readings, one when the disk completely covered the orb of the sun, the other when it just failed to do so. Tangents were drawn from the eye to the disk. The first reading necessarily gave him too big an angle, the second too small a one. The correct one lay somewhere between the two. An effort was also made to correct the error due to the fact that one sees not with a point but with an area of the eye. The experiment deserves to stand with those of Strato, exhibiting, as it does, the construction of apparatus for a specific purpose and the taking of precautions to guard against error in its use.

When we come, however, to examine from a proper perspective the character of the scientific achievement of this uniquely great man we can see that it shows a certain weakness due to the effect on it of the uncontrolled admiration for the logical consistency of geometry. We can best understand this by a comparison of Archimedes' work on *Statics* with the Aristotelian treatise on *Mechanics* already described. The Aristotelian, or rather pseudo-Aristotelian, work shows the science of mechanics at a more elementary and groping stage than that to which Archimedes brought it, but it is also more comprehensive and more enterprising. The reader will remember the great range of problems tackled by the earlier treatise, problems both of statics and dynamics. An effort was made to bring unity into this vast field of events by interpreting all of them in the light of the marvellous properties of the circle. 'Therefore, as has already been remarked, there is nothing to be surprised at in the circle being the principle behind all these wonders. The facts about the balance depend upon the circle, those about the lever depend upon the balance, and pretty well all the other problems of mechanical movement depend upon the lever.' (*Mechanical Problems*, 848a.) No such boldness characterizes the attempt of Archimedes. He had invented many weight-throwing engines, but he does not study ballistics. He had too wholesome an awareness of the logical difficulties that beset the idea of motion. He was about to constitute a science, and a science as he conceived it required to be presented as an orderly logical deduction from a limited number of clearly intelligible postulates. Archimedes accordingly put dynamics on one side and confined his attention to statics. Thus he produced his justly admired masterpiece. But Pierre Duhem (*Origines de la Statique*, Vol. I, p. 11) was right to observe and Arnold Reymond, in an excellently argued chapter (*Science in Greco-Roman Antiquity*, p. 195), was right to repeat, that 'The path followed by Archimedes in mechanics, though an admirable method of demonstration, is not a method of investigation. The certainty and lucidity of his principles are largely due to the fact that they are gathered, so to speak, from the surface of phenomena and not dug out from the depths.'

This excessive admiration for the purely logical in science must, if it is to be understood, be connected with the whole character of the society in which it grew. The reverse of the medal was contempt for the practical applications of science. Archimedes was the greatest engineer in antiquity, but when he was asked to write a handbook on engineering he refused (Plutarch, *Life of Marcellus*, chap. xvii). 'He looked upon the work of an engineer and everything that ministers to the needs of life as ignoble and vulgar', and wished his renown with posterity to rest entirely on his contribution to pure theory. It is an ironical judgment of history that his logically perfect treatise on statics should come to be regarded as less profound and less rich in promise of fruitful developments than the immature and disorderly work in the Aristotelian corpus.

ASTRONOMERS

The brilliant work of the Alexandrian astronomers also will reveal to us certain deficiencies not unconnected with the social conditions of the age. In our first volume we traced the history of Plato's famous formulation of the chief problem of astronomy. Whatever the *apparent* movements of the heavenly bodies might be Plato was convinced on religious grounds that the *true* movements must be revolutions at uniform speed in perfect circles. The problem was accordingly formulated in these terms: 'What are the uniform and ordered circular movements by the assumption of which the apparent movements of the planets can be accounted for?' We have told how the solution of this problem by Eudoxus, Callipus and Aristotle led to a view of the universe as consisting of fifty-nine concentric spheres, with the earth at the centre and the heaven of the fixed stars in the outermost place.

We have now to consider what the apparent irregularities were that required to be accounted for on Plato's assumptions. They affected more than the planets, as Plato knew. In his *Laws* (vii, 822a) he says that it is impious to use the term 'planets' (wanderers or vagabonds) of the gods in heaven, as if the so-called planets *and the sun and moon* never kept to one uniform course, but wandered hither and thither. More is therefore involved than the fact that the planets seem to vary in their speed, to stop and to regress. The further facts are that both the *moon* and the planets appear to vary in their distance from the ecliptic; and that even the *sun's* speed is not uniform. If the sun moves in a circle at uniform speed the four seasons ought to be exactly equal. But so soon as it became possible to determine the sun's arrival at the two solstices and the two equinoxes with approximate accuracy it became apparent that the seasons vary notably in length.

This variation had been established by the Athenian astronomer Meton a few years before the birth of Plato in 428, the phenomenon continued to be the subject of anxious investigation, and a hundred years later, in 330 b.c., we have on record an observation of the lengths of the seasons for that year which is within half a day the same as our modern calculation. Such were the observed irregularities which the contrivers of the ever more complicated system of homocentric spheres were forced to take into account. These were the phenomena which they had to save, as the phrase went. The inner tension produced by the contradiction between the observed facts and the mathematico-religious basis of their world-outlook resembles that produced in the nineteenth century by the contradiction between the narrative of the creation in Genesis and the new geological and biological knowledge.

Plato in his *Timaeus* (39 B–D) speaks of the 'wanderings' of the planets as 'incalculable in multitude and marvellously intricate'. On this Heath comments (*Aristarchus of Samos,* p. 171), this admission 'is in sharp contrast to the assumption of the spirals regularly described on spheres of which the independent orbits are great circles, and still more to the assertion in the *Laws* that it is wrong and even impious to speak of the planets as "wandering" at all, since "each of them traverses the same path, not many paths, but always one circular path". For the moment,' continues Heath, 'Plato condescends to use the language of *apparent* astronomy, the astronomy of observation; and this may remind us that Plato's astronomy, even in its latest form as expounded in the *Timaeus* and the *Laws,* is consciously and intentionally ideal.'

It is an odd compliment to Plato's pre-eminence as an idealist to describe as 'ideal' his obstinate adherence on religious grounds to an unworkable hypothesis. Heath (*Op. cit.,*

p. 200) is less ceremonious with Eudoxus, who first worked
the homocentric system out. 'Eudoxus,' he writes, 'supposed
the annual motion of the sun to be perfectly uniform; he
must therefore have deliberately ignored the discovery made
by Meton and Euctemon sixty or seventy years before, that
the sun does not take the same time to describe the four
quadrants of its orbit between the equinoctial and solstitial
points.' But when inconvenient discoveries continued to
multiply, a breach was at last made in the conception of a
geocentric universe with the heavenly bodies moving round
a stationary earth in homocentric spheres. The daring inno-
vator was an associate of the Academy, Heraclides of Pontus
(388–310). He introduced two revolutionary ideas. Taking
account of the fact that the planets Venus and Mercury are
never observed to be at any great angular distance from the
sun, he suggested (1) the explanation that they revolve not
about the earth, but about the sun. He added (2) that the
appearance of a daily revolution of the heavens about the
earth could equally well be explained on the assumption of a
daily rotation of the earth about its axis. These were two very
disturbing suggestions. They shook the foundations of the
universe in two ways, first by making the sun into a second
centre, and then by making the old fixed centre, the earth,
rotate.

These were difficult concessions to make to the science of
observation. Readers should remember that the mathematico-
religious conception of the universe, based on the properties
of the circle and the sphere, had fought a tough battle to
establish itself against a rival view. The atomists believed in
an infinity of worlds coming into existence and passing away
in boundless space. The Pythagoreans and Platonists believed
in the uniqueness, the eternity, and the finiteness of our universe. The innovations of Heraclides seemed like dangerous
concessions to the atomistic view. Such was the state of the

science of astronomy when the work of the Alexandrian astronomers began.

Heraclides of Pontus was a resident at Athens. The first of the great Alexandrian astronomers was Aristarchus of Samos, a pupil of Strato of Lampsacus. His probable dates are 310–230, which makes him about seventy-five years younger than Heraclides and twenty-five years older than Archimedes. He will be for ever remembered as the first to put forward the heliocentric hypothesis. Copernicus, in the sixteenth century, was aware that he was reviving the hypothesis of Aristarchus. Though the treatise in which Aristarchus developed his hypothesis is lost, we have the most reliable testimony to its existence. His younger contemporary Archimedes, in that interesting work to which we have made so much reference, the *Sand-reckoner*, tells us that Aristarchus published a book containing a number of hypotheses, among which was the following : *the fixed stars and the sun remain unmoved, but the earth revolves about the sun in the circumference of a circle, the sun lying in the middle of the orbit.* Though Aristarchus still adhered to circular motion, and though it is improbable that his suggestion was put forward as more than a mathematical hypothesis, we have evidence of the shock it caused. Cleanthes, the head of the Stoic school at Athens, a man devoutly attached to star-worship, who was his almost exact contemporary (the two men died old within a year or two of one another), expressed the opinion that the Greeks ought to indict Aristarchus on a charge of impiety. These threats of the philosophic schools (Cleanthes was only reasserting the argument of Plato in the *Laws*) appear to have involved a real danger to the scientist. Such is the opinion of sober historians like Paul Tannéry and Pierre Duhem (Duhem, *Système du Monde* 1, 425). In all antiquity only one astronomer, Seleucus, a Babylonian, who lived about a hundred years after Aristarchus, was found to support his hypothesis. He, indeed, went further, and apparently asserted his belief in it not only as a mathematical hypothesis but as a physical fact. But one swallow does not make a summer. The conception of a heliocentric universe was still-born.

The treatise in which Aristarchus developed this hypothesis is, as we have said, lost. But another of his writings, *On the Sizes and Distances of the Sun and Moon,* is still extant. It is judged to be an earlier work by reason of the fact that it contains no allusion to the heliocentric hypothesis and bases part of its argument on a very faulty estimate of the angle subtended at the eye by the orb of the sun, an estimate corrected by Aristarchus himself elsewhere. But it offers such an admirable and typical example of Alexandrian science that we shall give a brief description of it. T. L. Heath's edition of the text in his *Aristarchus of Samos* is one of the modern classics in the history of science.

The book begins in the orderly Alexandrian fashion with a list of six hypotheses which form the basis of the whole argument.

1. That the moon receives its light from the sun.

2. That the earth is in the relation of a point and centre to the sphere in which the moon moves.

3. That when the moon appears to us halved, the great circle which divides the dark and the bright portions of the moon is in the direction of our eye. (That is, the centres of the sun, earth and moon form a right-angled triangle, with the right angle at the centre of the moon.)

4. That when the moon appears to us halved, its distance from the sun is then less than a quadrant by one thirtieth of a quadrant. (This estimate of the moon's angular distance from the sun, 87 degrees, is very much out. The true angle is over 89 degrees.)

5. That the breadth of the earth's shadow is that of two moons.

6. That the moon subtends one-fifteenth part of a sign of the zodiac. (This again is wrong. As we have already seen, Archimedes reports a later, and pretty accurate, estimate of Aristarchus, reducing his estimate of 2 degrees to half a degree.)

Aristarchus then proceeds to establish eighteen propositions, the most important of which are these :

1. The distance of the sun from the earth is greater than eighteen times, but less than twenty times, the distance of the moon from the earth.

2. The diameter of the sun is greater than eighteen times, but less than twenty times, the diameter of the moon.

3. The diameter of the sun has to the diameter of the earth a ratio greater than 19 : 3 but less than 43 : 6.

Aristarchus had attempted only comparisons between the sizes of sun, moon and earth. Estimates in standard units of measurement were still lacking, or, if not wholly lacking, inadequate. The next great Alexandrian astronomer and geographer, Eratosthenes (about 284–192), supplied the lack. He observed that at Syene (the modern Assuan) at noon at the summer solstice, the sun is directly overhead, while at Alexandria, roughly 5,000 stades away and roughly on the same meridian, the sun-dial showed the sun at a distance from the zenith of one-fiftieth of the meridian circle. This gives a length of 250,000 stades for the earth's circumference, and if we give Eratosthenes the benefit of the doubt as to which particular measurement called the stade he was working with, his polar diameter of the earth works out at only about fifty miles short of our modern estimate.

GEOGRAPHERS

With Eratosthenes the science of mathematical and astronomical geography was constituted. In its rise from its humble beginnings geography had shared the rapidity which characterizes the development of other Greek sciences. No doubt there had been much preparatory work done by nameless, or all but nameless, men in many parts of the Greek world. Astronomy itself had been advanced in this way. In a work on *Weather Signs* Theophrastus writes: 'Good heed must be taken of the local conditions of the region in which one is placed. It is, however, always possible to find a local observer, and the signs learnt from such persons are the most trustworthy. Thus good astronomers have been found in some parts – for instance, Matricetas at Methymna observed the solstices from Mount Lepetymnos, Cleostratus in Tenedos from Mount Ida, Phaeinos at Athens from Mount Lycabettus. Meton, who made the calendar cycle of nineteen years, was the pupil of the last named. Phaeinos was a resident alien at Athens. Other examples of local astronomers could be given.'[4] Similarly the harbours and coasts of the Mediterranean must have been described and mapped in a crude way by generations of mariners before the scientific works began. Anaximander, as we have related in our first volume, was the first to make a map *of the world*. He is very unlikely to have been the first to make a map of a harbour or a stretch of coast. In later times Greek geographers refer frequently to documents called *Harbours* and *Coasting Voyages* (*limenes* and *periploi*). Richard Uhden (*Imago Mundi,* vol. i, pp. 2 and 3) argues convincingly for these being not books but maps.

However this may be, and however early we may suppose such local map-making to have begun, from the time of Anaximander on Greek geography has a distinguished history of rapid development. The younger contemporary and fellow-townsman of Anaximander, Hecataeus, wrote a *De-*

4. Theophrastus, Loeb ed., vol. II, p. 393.

scription of the World. The history of Herodotus is full of geographical information. Eudoxus wrote a second *Description of the World*. Aristotle's *Meteorology* contains much of geographical interest, and his pupil Dicaearchus was famous for a map of the inhabited earth and for reasonable estimates of the heights of mountains.

Out of all this activity gradually emerged a picture of a geographical globe with poles, equator, ecliptic, tropics, meridians of longitude and parallels of latitude. Five zones were recognized – frigid zones at the poles, a torrid zone about the equator and two temperate zones, though the extent of these zones was at first variable, being fixed rather by meteorological than by astronomical indications. The progress of astronomical geography was furthered both by the invention of astronomical instruments – Aristarchus, for instance, is credited with an improved sun-dial – and, at least in one famous instance, by the voyage of a sailor who combined scientific and commercial enthusiasm. Between the years 310 and 306, when the Carthaginians, who normally controlled the western end of the Mediterranean, were locked in a deadly struggle with the Sicilian Greeks, Pytheas, a Greek sailor of Marseilles, slipped through the Pillars of Hercules and made for Cornwall to investigate the possibilities of the tin-trade. His voyage probably took him as far as Norway and the Baltic, and he seized the opportunity to calculate a number of fresh latitudes. There is no doubt that his achievement had its effect on the geographical science of Eratosthenes.

From now on a general acquaintance with astronomical geography was part of the education of the citizen, and geographical science in its two main divisions – descriptive and mathematical – was necessary to the successful administration of states. The best ancient geographical treatise we possess, that by Strabo (eight vols. in the Loeb Library), was

composed between 9 and 5 b.c., probably in the interest of
Pythodoris, Queen of Pontus. An earlier residence of some
four or five years in Alexandria had given him access to the
best sources of material, from which (wherever he read them)
he quotes abundantly. After explaining that his work will
be mainly descriptive, Strabo expresses himself as follows :
'The reader, however, should not be so unsophisticated or
idle as never to have studied a globe and its circles, some
parallel, others at right angles to the parallels, others again
oblique. He should know the position of the tropics, equator
and zodiac. With a matriculation knowledge of these things
– the horizons, arctic circles and so forth – he will be able to
follow the book. But if he doesn't even know what a straight
line is, or a curve or a circle, or the difference between a
spherical and a plane surface, and cannot even pick out the
seven stars of the Bear in the night sky, my book will be no
use to him – or none just yet. He must first acquaint himself
with the studies preparatory to a knowledge of geography.
It is also this lack of preliminary training that makes the
work of the authors of the so-called *Harbours* and *Coasting
Voyages* incomplete. They fail to supply the relevant mathematical and astronomical details.' (I, 1, 21.)

ASTRONOMY AGAIN

We must now leave the contribution made by astronomy to
geography and return to astronomy itself. It is not only the
greatest scientific achievement of the Alexandrian age, but
the special form of its development reveals best the action of
the prevailing philosophy on the science of the time. We have
seen the astronomers uneasily ignoring irregularities in the
movements of the heavenly bodies for which they had failed
to account. But their situation was more difficult than we
have yet disclosed. It was not only that there were phenomena

still unaccounted for, there were phenomena which on their hypothesis could never be accounted for. The blunt fact is that the homocentric hypothesis was, in its fundamental principle, unacceptable and that the reasons for its inadmissibility were generally known by those who nevertheless laboured to perfect it.

The homocentric system, if true, implied that every one of the heavenly bodies maintains an unvarying distance from the earth. They move *round* the earth, they do not approach or depart from it. But the distance of the planets from the earth in fact varies every day, as is plainly visible with Venus and Mars by the variations in their brightness. The distance of the moon varies, as is clear from the measurable variations in its apparent diameter. Such variations are also proved by the fact of eclipses of the sun being sometimes annular (when the moon is too far from the earth to cover the sun completely) and sometimes total (when the moon is nearer to the earth). Such variations also follow from the fact of the variations in speed of the heavenly bodies. If the angular speed of a heavenly body varies, it is because we are not observing it from the centre round which it revolves.

How early were these facts known? Listen to the words of an astronomer, Sosigenes, of the second century A.D. who had access to the ancient books now lost to us. 'The spheres of the partisans of Eudoxus do not account for the phenomena. Not only do they not account for the phenomena which have been discovered after them, *they do not account for the phenomena which were known before them and which they themselves regarded as true.* Can Eudoxus, can Calippus, be said to have succeeded? There is one thing at least, plain to the view, that none of them succeeded in deducing from his hypotheses. I refer to the fact that certain stars are sometimes near to us and sometimes far. This can be seen in the case of Venus and Mars, which show much bigger in the middle of their retrograde path, so much so that, on moonless nights, Venus casts shadows. The same variations can be observed in the moon, if we compare it with objects invariable in size. Those who use instruments confirm this observation. At the same distance from the observer it sometimes takes a disk of eleven fingers' breadth to shut out the moon, sometimes of twelve. Observations on eclipses of the sun tell the same tale. Sometimes the sun remains for some time hidden by the moon, sometimes the moon does not completely cover the sun. The same conclusion also follows from the daily variations in the apparent speeds of the heavenly bodies. Now these appearances the followers of Eudoxus have not accounted for. They have not even tried to explain the variations in speed, although it is a problem that deserves attention. *One cannot say that they did not know the variations in the distance of the same star. Polemarchus of Cyzicus knew the variations, but dismissed them as of no importance because he had a prejudice in favour of the system which arranges all the spheres concentrically about the centre of the Universe.* It is clear also that Aristotle, in his *Physical Problems*, doubted the hypotheses of the astronomers because the size of the planets does not remain the same.'

Such is the account of Sosigenes. It records a crisis of thought at the end of the fourth century in the Academy and the Lyceum at Athens. The account of Sosigenes is based, at least in part, on the history of astronomy by Aristotle's pupil Eudemus, and the men he mentions as having discussed, or evaded, the problem – Eudoxus, Calippus, Polemarchus, Aristotle, and others whose names we have omitted in our shortened version – belong to this period. It was as the aftermath of this controversy, with its establishment of the homocentric system on the basis of ignoring inconvenient facts, that the systems of Heraclides and Aristarchus broke away from the orthodox view, and by making some planets revolve about the sun or by making the earth itself revolve about the sun, attempted to account for some at least of the unexplained phenomena. But, as we have seen, the fear of dislodging the earth from the centre of the universe was too great. Their effort failed. The heliocentric system was finally abandoned so far as the ancient world was concerned.

If we look into this question more closely we shall find much matter for wonder. The system of homocentric spheres was known to be false at the very time when it was being constituted by Eudoxus and Calippus. Nevertheless it reigned, if not unchallenged at least unshaken, for some two thousand years. What is the explanation? The explanation lies in the more general philosophical conceptions into the framework of which astronomy had to be made to fit. Aristotle had written a work *On The Heavens*. This is not an astronomical work, but a physical work, in the sense in which the *Timaeus* of Plato is a treatise on physics. That is to say, it is theological and deductive in character. In this work *On The Heavens* Aristotle argues that since the activity of God is eternal life, and since the heavens are divine, the motion of the heavens must be eternal, and therefore the heavens must be a rotating sphere. Further, since the centre of a rotating body is at rest, the earth must be at rest in the centre of the universe. The earth, which is the realm of change, consists of the elements of Earth, Air, Fire and Water, but the heavenly bodies, which are eternal, consist of a Fifth Element, free from change, free from generation and decay, and moving not like the terrestrial elements in a straight line but in a circle.

Such in the Pythagorean, Platonic, early Aristotelian and Stoic conceptions was the nature of the universe. The starry heavens were the visible image of the divine. As such they shared the lot of the gods and became the province of the theologian. They were called upon in a special sense to be the revelation of the divine mind to man and they played a multiple role in the government of cities and empires. The stability of ancient oligarchical society was bound up with a particular view of astronomy. To hold other views was not a scientific error but a heresy. Astronomy in antiquity was as thorny a subject as biblical criticism in modern times. Observational astronomy was subjected to anxious scrutiny and careful management. One had to be as indiscreet as Colenso or as stubborn as Loisy to ignore the convention. The wanderings of the planets, the variations in the lengths of the seasons, the changes in the distances of the heavenly bodies from the earth were awkward subjects, like miracles, forgeries, or persecution. The astronomers themselves were often torn between two loyalties, like modern historians of religion. They had scientific consciences, but they knew that they were trespassing on a field where opinion involved political and social consequences. Often their own personal religious convictions were at variance with the facts of observation. Belief in the star gods was sincerely and passionately held by many exalted minds.

For these reasons we need not be surprised that efforts to alter astronomical conceptions on the basis of an observational science, the authority of which was still very insecurely established in all but the rarest minds, should encounter violent resistance not only among priests, philosophers and kings, but even among astronomers. 'The obstacles which in the seventeenth century Protestantism and then the Catholic Church', writes Duhem, 'offered to the progress of the Copernican doctrine can only give us a feeble idea of the accusations of impiety that ancient Paganism would have levelled at the bold mortal who dared to shake the perpetual immobility of Earth, the Hearth of the Gods, and to assimilate the incorruptible and divine being of the stars to that of Earth, the lowly domain of generation and of death.' (*Op.*

cit., I, 425.) Only the Epicureans consistently maintained and uttered such blasphemies, insisting that the heavens had a beginning and would have an end, that the heavenly bodies so far from being divine were masses of dead matter. And they had difficulty in reassuring their followers that those who proposed such views were not in danger of being damned for them (Lucretius, V, 110–25). It was for such reasons as these that ancient astronomy rejected the aberrations of Heraclides and Aristarchus and returned to the conception of a geocentric universe.

This did mean a delay in the formation of truer opinions on the shape and size of the universe, and it checked mechanical and chemical speculation on the motion and substance of the heavenly bodies. It caused no interruption to the pursuit of positional astronomy and the improvement of the calendar. Here one may safely rally to the conviction of the poet Rossetti, that 'it makes not the slightest difference to anybody whether the earth goes round the sun or the sun round the earth'. On the latter hypothesis was based the work of the great astronomer, Hipparchus, in the opinion of many the greatest astronomer in the ancient world, to whose system we must now turn.

The theory of eccentrics and epicycles, which forms the basis both of the system of Hipparchus (died about 125 B.C.) and Ptolemy (died after A.D. 161), was probably the invention of late Pythagorean schools in South Italy, from where it made its way to Alexandria. The new principles can be readily understood in their simplest forms, though their complete elaboration in the *Syntaxis* of Ptolemy presents a formidable study. If we stick to the assumption that the sun moves in a perfect circle at uniform speed, then the only explanation of its variations in angular velocity as observed by us is that *we are not ourselves situated at the centre of the circle in which it revolves*. The sun's circle is eccentric to the earth. This theory involves the necessity of supposing that a body like the sun can revolve about a geometrical point, which was a difficult conception for the ancient astronomer, but it became the accepted explanation. The theory of the epicycle is a little more complex. Consider the movements of the planet Venus. Two movements have got to be accounted for – the synodic revolution, when Venus returns to the same position relative to the sun and earth, and the zodiacal revolution. The supposition that Venus revolves in a circle about a point which itself revolves about the earth provides an explanation of both these movements. The first circle is the *epicycle*. Venus completes her revolution in this circle in the time of the synodic revolution. The larger circle, described by the centre of the epicycle about the earth's centre, is the *deferent*. The centre of the epicycle completes this revolution in the time of the zodiacal revolution of the planet. A radius from the centre of the earth extended to the centre of the sun passes through the centre of the epicycle. The radius of the epicycle is given by the maximum distance of Venus's departure from the sun.

A similar scheme would apply to the planet Mercury, which also remains in the neighbourhood of the sun. In the case of the planets which do not remain in the neighbourhood of the sun it is no longer possible to suppose that a radius of the earth which passes through the centre of the epicycle will always pass through the centre of the sun, for each of these planets has a longer zodiacal period than the sun, thirty years for Saturn, twelve for Jupiter, two for Mars, to quote the estimates known to Eudoxus. But the hypotheses may be generalized to include all the planets as follows: To each planet corresponds a deferent circle, lying in the plane of the ecliptic, and having for centre the centre of the earth. This deferent circle is described by a point which is the centre of the epicycle in which the planet moves.

The time taken to describe the deferent is the zodiacal period. The time taken to describe the epicycle is the synodic period.

Alexandrian astronomy had also its more practical side. Nowadays we take the calendar for granted, but the calendar was not an easy thing to perfect – if we can yet call it perfect when an important body of opinion is asking for its reform. The Greek astronomer Geminus who is thought to have written about 70 B.C. defines the main problem when he says: 'The ancients had before them the problem of reckoning the months by the moon but the years by the sun.' This bringing into harmony of the older method of reckoning time by the moon with the later method by means of the sun and so establishing a lunisolar calendar is one of the achievements of ancient civilization for which a share of credit goes to the Greeks, although some would maintain that they did little more than serve as a connecting link between the scientific achievement of Babylonia and the civil needs of the Roman empire. As we know, the solar year is 365¼ days approximately, while the month is approximately 29½ days. No round number of months to the year will make these two correspond. A twelve-month year will give us 354 days, which is eleven days short by the sun. The desert Arabs still get on very well with this system. The fact that they have gained nearly forty years since the date of the Hegira (622) is of no practical importance to them. But very early in the history of the civilization of the Near East efforts were made to find a cycle of years in which the lunar and solar years would correspond. In the eighth century the Greeks borrowed from the Babylonians an eight-year cycle. Three hundred years later, in 432 B.C., the astronomer Meton introduced a nineteen-year cycle to the notice of the Athenians. This probably also had its origin in Babylonia. It is a very efficient system, keeping the lunar and solar calendars in step for over two hundred years before they require adjustment by a single day. But the modern evidence is that the Athenians did not in practice observe it – one of many indications that administration in ancient time was less efficient than it is to-day. A hundred years later Calippus devised a seventy-six-year cycle. Two hundred years after that again Hipparchus came forward with a cycle of 304 years. These refinements were of more interest to astronomers – perhaps to astrologers – than to the framers of the civil calendar, but it must be borne in mind that when Julius Caesar wanted to reform the civil calendar of Rome he sent to Alexandria for an expert who made an excellent job of it.

Almost all the writings of Hipparchus are lost, but we know from the evidence of Ptolemy that three of them had reference to the calendar or to problems that arose out of its improvement. These were : *Intercalary Months and Days, On the Length of the Year, On the Movement of the Solstitial and Equinoctial Points*. In his efforts to determine as accurately as possible the length of the year Hipparchus disclosed the difference between the tropic and the sidereal year and thus discovered, and indeed measured with astonishing accuracy, the phenomenon of the precession of the equinoxes. Modern astronomy tells us that, owing to the bulge of the earth at the equator, the earth oscillates slightly in its revolution about its axis. The effect of this oscillation is that the pole of the earth is not steady but moves in a circle, completing a revolution once in every twenty-six thousand years. The effect of this oscillation is to produce a slight alteration in the position of the sun and planets as seen from the earth against the background of the fixed stars. It was this alteration that was detected by Hipparchus. He made determinations of the tropical year, that is the interval of time which separates two successive arrivals of the sun at the same equinoctial point. He made determinations also of the sidereal year, that is of the time it takes the sun to return to the same star. Comparing his findings with the records of earlier astronomers he noticed that an equinoctial point does not throughout the centuries retain the same relation to a fixed star but slowly moves forward along the zodiacal belt from East to West. Hence the name of the Precession of the Equinoxes. In his book on the length of the year Hipparchus says that the precession is not less than a degree in a century. In his later work on the precession he arrives at a more precise determination, given by Tannéry as 1 degree, 23 minutes, 20 seconds. The modern estimate is only 10 seconds more.

In arriving at these accurate determinations Hipparchus is thought to have had Babylonian as well as earlier Greek records to work upon. Whatever advantages he enjoyed, he had achieved results which fill us with awe, and set a standard of scientific work to which remote generations may look back with pride. So sensible was Hipparchus of the debt he owed to his predecessors, so well aware was he that only records kept over the generations make possible a conclusion so refined as that of the precession of the equinoxes, that he too determined to leave posterity in his debt and busied himself to make calculations of the positions of some eight hundred and fifty of the fixed stars, together with some record of their appearances, so that future astronomers might be able to detect changes. 'He made the heavens our common heritage', comments old Pliny, 'supposing anybody could be found great enough to enter on the inheritance.' (*Natural History*, II, 26, 95.)

It is unfortunate that the one treatise by Hipparchus which has survived should not be among the most important or interesting of his works. Nevertheless it tells us something of the time, and we shall briefly describe it. About the year 270 B.C. a versifier of great skill, Aratus, had composed a didactic poem on astronomy, which continued throughout antiquity to enjoy great popularity. A young friend wrote to Hipparchus to be informed of the degree of accuracy of this widely influential poem. Hipparchus, in reply, after complimenting his friend on the steadfastness of his interest in science, first establishes the general point that the poet Aratus had relied for his facts on the astronomer Eudoxus. He then proceeds to criticize Eudoxus in the light of later knowledge. This is not without interest as an example will show. 'Eudoxus displays ignorance about the North Pole in the following passage. "There is a star which remains always motionless. This star is the pole of the world." In fact there is no star at the pole but an empty space close to which lie three stars, which, taken together with the point at the pole, make a rough quadrangle, as Pytheas of Marseilles tells us.' (*Commentary on Aratus*, I, iv, 1.)

THE ORGANIZATION OF LEARNING

The mention of this commentary on a poem which had been written about a hundred and thirty years before serves as a reminder of a function of the Museum which must by no means be omitted from our account. We have spoken of the fact that the Library connected with the Museum contained about half a million rolls. This might easily lead to an exaggerated notion of the extent of the world's literature at this time. It must be remembered that a Homer, which with us can be made up into a compact volume that will fit in the pocket, would then occupy fifty or more rolls. But, if there is danger of exaggerating the number of books that then existed, there is no likelihood that we shall exaggerate the role of the Museum in creating the whole technique, apparatus and tradition of scholarship. A famous modern scholar, Boeckh, described the ideal of what the Germans call Philology as 'the systematic knowledge of what has been known'

– *Erkenntniss des Erkannten, cogniti cognitio.* This task of scholarship, which is of priceless importance to the human race, as being the indispensable foundation of historical knowledge, was first adequately cared for by the Museum. The British public at the present day is probably much better fitted to understand the importance of the natural sciences than the historical. It is better fitted to understand what science means than to understand what scholarship means. Many have felt in their own minds the transforming power of scientific conceptions and of a scientific attitude to life. They know by their own experience that a man who has learned the technique of scientific investigation has added a new power to his mind. Far fewer are they who have been touched by any similar attitude to scholarship, who have felt that the systematic knowledge of what has been known is not a dead thing but the most living of all things, raising human consciousness, as it were, to a new dimension. The rub is that so few of the scholars have any sense of this truth themselves. Collingwood was not talking idly when he said (*Autobiography*, Pelican ed., p. 61): 'In the last thirty or forty years historical thought had been achieving an acceleration in the velocity of its progress and an enlargement in its outlook comparable to those which natural science had achieved about the beginning of the seventeenth century. It seemed to me as nearly certain as anything in the future could be, that historical thought, whose constantly increasing importance had been one of the most striking features of the nineteenth century, would increase in importance far more rapidly during the twentieth; and that we might very well be standing on the threshold of an age in which history would be as important for the world as natural science had been between 1600 and 1900.' Such an extension of the range of human thinking as Collingwood here foreshadows could not even have been glimpsed if the Museum had not made distant preparation for it by inventing the technique of the preservation, criticism and accurate transmission of texts.

GRAMMAR

Out of this care for the written record of the past emerged a great achievement of Alexandrian science, Grammar. The complicated phenomena of speech are not easy to analyse and the eventual emergence of a science of grammar had been prepared for by generations of curious enquiry and practical endeavour. The difficulty of these obscure steps escapes the casual eye. Accepting the marvel of the Phoenician invention of a phonetic alphabet, we have still to enquire how the Greeks took the measure of the problem of borrowing the script and adapting it to their own requirements. Eduard Schwyzer[5] opines that the practical phonetics implicit in the recitation of cult hymns and the Homeric poems were a necessary preparation for the application of a foreign alphabet to the writing of Greek. However that may be, we have evidence that the Ionian Greeks in the sixth century had become grammar conscious. They had begun to pay attention to the declension of nouns and had a doctrine of cases. The fifth-century philosophers thought hard on linguistic problems. All the phenomena of speech have entered into full consciousness. They are busy with letters, syllables, words, rhythm, style. There is division of opinion on the tremendous question whether languages are established by nature or by convention. Plato, in his *Cratylus*, debated the question with characteristic range and subtlety. With characteristic perversity, too, be it added, for he introduced the extravagant theory, sharply criticized by Lucretius (Bk. V, 1041ff.) that words were invented by a Lawgiver and passed

5. *Griechische Grammatik*, p. 5.

as fit for current use by a Metaphysician! Aristotle, the Stoics and the Epicureans carried on the work of linguistic analysis. It remained for the Alexandrians in this as in other departments of knowledge to give the subject systematic form.

The earliest text-book of grammar that has come down to us is by one Denys of Thrace (or Dionysius Thrax, to give him his Latin name). It shows all the genius of the age by its clear definition of grammar as 'the practical knowledge of the usage of the writers of poetry and prose'. It is obvious from the chief divisions of the work that it has acquired its form from its function. Greek literature when Dionysius made his grammar was already six hundred years old. The language had changed with the passage of time. The literature had been created through the medium of a considerable variety of dialects. It was now being studied by non-Greeks all over the Mediterranean world. An aid to study was required. Accordingly the grammar of Dionysius, the aim of which was to give a practical knowledge of correct usage, dealt with accurate reading, explanation of figures of speech, exposition of rare words and subject-matter, etymology, doctrine of the regular grammatical forms, and finally, criticism of poetry, which is described as 'the noblest part of all'. Two specimens of the contents will be given. (1) The parts of speech are defined as: noun, verb, participle, article, pronoun, preposition, adverb and conjunction. (2) Reading is said to be 'the delivery without stumbling of poetry or prose'. Then the instruction follows: 'In reading aloud one must attend to the manner of the delivery, to the accentuation and to the punctuation. From the manner of delivery we tell the character of the work, from the accentuation the skill in composition, from the punctuation the thought contained in it. Our aim must be to read tragedy in an heroic manner, comedy in an everyday style, elegy plaintively, epic firmly, lyric musically, laments in a subdued and tearful way. What is done in disregard of these rules defeats the intention of the poet and brings ridicule on the art of the reader.' What an admirable grammar this is! Sure in taste, firm in doctrine, concise in presentation, clear in aim, it held its own for some thirteen centuries, a monument both to the high literary character of the civilization of Greece and to the mastery of the Alexandrians over the difficult art of the textbook.

We are now coming to the end of the first period of Alexandrian science and it will be an appropriate moment to take a general view of it. Towards the end of the third century A.D. a Christian bishop, Anatolius of Laodicea, delivered himself of some broad generalizations on the development of Greek science which it will be helpful to consider. He remarked that in the time of the Pythagoreans, which we would interpret to include Plato and his school, philosophers thought they ought to concern themselves only with the eternal and changeless reality, free from any other admixture. But at a more recent date, he continued, mathematicians changed their opinion and began to busy themselves not only with the incorporeal and ideal, but also with the corporal and sensible. 'In a word', he writes, 'the mathematician must now be skilled in the theory of the movement of the stars, their speeds, their sizes, their constellations, their distances. Furthermore he must instruct himself in the various modifications of vision. He must know the reasons why objects do not at every distance appear what they are in reality; why, though they keep their mutual relations, they produce illusory appearances as to their positions and order, whether in sky or air, or in mirrors and other polished surfaces, or seen through transparent media. Again it is now believed that the mathematician must be an engineer and must understand geodesy and calculation and be concerned with the combination of sounds to form agreeable melody.'

The subjects here stressed – astronomy, optics, mechanics, geodesy, applied arithmetic, harmonics – remind us of the practical aspect science had assumed in its journey from Plato's Academy via the Lyceum of Aristotle to the Museum of Ctesibius and Archimedes. It also indicates a major omission from the list of sciences we have so far described, namely optics. This very important subject, treated many times by Alexandrian scientists from Euclid to Ptolemy, was divided into four main heads: Optics proper, Catoptrics, Dioptrics, and Scenography. The first dealt with what we would now call perspective, the visual effects produced by viewing objects from various distances and angles. *Catoptrics* dealt with effects produced on rays of light by reflecting or transparent media, that is to say with reflection in mirrors, formation of rainbows, light seen through a prism, burning-glasses, and so forth. We can best understand what was included in *Dioptrics* by an examination of the treatise of Hero of Alexandria on the surveyor's instrument called the Dioptra, which took the place with the ancients of our theodolite. It deals with such problems as : to determine the difference of level between two given points ; to bore a tunnel through a mountain beginning from both ends ; to construct a harbour on the model of a given segment of a circle, given the two ends. The fourth, *Scenography*, is the application of perspective whether to genuine architecture or to stage scenery. It dealt with the whole fascinating subject which is opened up to us by these words of an eighth-century writer : 'The object of the architect is to produce a work which is well-proportioned in appearance and, so far as possible, to contrive correctives for ocular illusions, setting before himself as his goal symmetry and proportion not in reality but as judged by the eye.' As is well known, this correction of ocular illusions was a practice of Greek architects, the secret of their wonderful results. Doubtless the traditional practice was systematized into a treatise in Alexandria, but no such treatise has come down to us.

We have said that the first two hundred years of the existence of the Museum were the most important. In fact, within less than that period from the foundation of Alexandria itself in 330, a crisis had overtaken the Museum with the description of which we shall bring this long chapter to a close. The ninth Ptolemy, who called himself Euergetes (or Benefactor) II but who was called by the Alexandrian Greeks Malefactor or Fat Belly, had a long and mysterious reign, from 146 to 117. From the monuments which survive it would appear that he did much good to Egypt in his long reign, but his career has suggested to the modern historian that he preferred to spend money on promoting Egyptian institutions rather than on financing foreign professors. The historian Polybius visited Alexandria during the reign of this king. He was disgusted with its state. He draws a sharp distinction between three elements in the population, the Egyptians, the now mongrel Greek ruling class, and the mercenary foreign soldiers. Polybius calls the native Egyptians an intelligent and civilized race. He says that the mercenary soldiers were out of hand and had forgotten how to obey. Of the third element in the population, he says that they, being originally Greek, had retained some recollection of Greek principles, but had been corrupted by their privileged position as against the natives. Then he adds that Fat Belly had almost exterminated them.

This persecution of the Greek element in Alexandria seems to be confirmed by the report from other sources (Athenaeus, IV, 83) that there was a great revival of learning in other Greek lands during the reign of this king, for he not only massacred many Alexandrians but exiled many more. ' The result was that all the cities and islands were filled with grammarians, philosophers, geometers, musicians, painters, trainers, physicians and other artists who being compelled by poverty to turn teachers produced many famous pupils.' It is relevant to point out that the great grammarian Dionysius appears to have written his grammar not at Alexandria but at Rhodes. He is probably to be regarded as one of the involuntary exiles. It is not to be supposed, however, that the Museum ceased to exist at this time. There is evidence, in fact, that, whatever the extent and the motive for his persecution of the Greeks, Ptolemy IX was a patron of learning and literature. Nevertheless his reign marks a turning-point. Not only were scientists, scholars and artists scattered far and wide, but Egypt and the whole of the Eastern Mediterranean world were now fallen within the shadow of Roman power and Rome itself had now for about a hundred years been busy with the creation of a literature of its own. The Romans had as yet produced no great work of science and were not ever destined to produce many. But their rulers were now cultivated men who were beginning to be interested in Greek and had the opportunity to be entertained at home by the native comedy of Plautus and Terence. Plautus and Terence, and the epic and didactic poet Ennius, had already carried over into Latin much of the sophisticated mind of Greece. Henceforth we shall be concerned not only with a Greek but a Graeco-Roman world.

And not only Graeco-Roman. When Roman political power swept the Mediterranean world into its orbit, of all the peoples it overran it found two, and only two, with literatures that were destined to survive and exercise mastery over the minds and the hearts of men – the Greeks and the Jews. Now it was in Alexandria that the penetration of the mind of Europe by the Hebrew scriptures began. There was accomplished a work which so far had no parallel in history, the translation of the literature of one civilization into that of another. Some are of opinion that the initiative in translating the Hebrew scriptures into Greek was due to the Ptolemies and the Museum. The more probable opinion is that the Alexandrian Jews, who were forgetting their native tongue, made the translation themselves for their own use in their synagogues. However that may be, first the Law and then the Prophets made their way into Greek. By the reign of Ptolemy Physcon (Fat Belly) the whole canon had been translated and the Greek Bible, the Septuagint, existed. It is not the subject of our book, but reckoned in terms of world influence it is as great and as typical a product of the first two hundred years of the existence of Alexandria as the science of Archimedes and Hipparchus. The mixture of Greek and Hebrew ideas in Alexandria supplied the background out of which Christianity was to arise. The Septuagint supplied the language in which its sacred books were to be written. Christianity was prepared for in Alexandria, it conquered Rome, it was to found Constantinople. We shall have occasion before we conclude to refer again to this all-important Alexandrian creation, the Greek Bible.

BIBLIOGRAPHICAL NOTE

On the general history of the Museum see Sandys, *History of Classical Scholarship*, Vol. I. For the science of the period T. L. Heath's two masterpieces, *History of Greek Mathematics* and *Aristarchus of Samos* are indispensable. So is Duhem, *Système du Monde*, Vols. I and II. A. de Rochas, *La Science des Philosophes et l'Art des Thaumaturges* is intelligent, clear, and full of out-of-the-way material, but neither so learned nor so reliable as Heath or Duhem. Jotham Johnson's article, *Calendars of Antiquity* (Journal of Calendar Reform, Dec. 1936), good in itself, contains valuable bibliographical indications. The best edition of the *Grammar* of Dionysius Thrax is by G. Uhlig, 1883.

CHAPTER THREE

*The Graeco-Roman Age – Bilingual culture: The Grammarian,
the Encyclopaedist, the Translator – Cicero and Lucretius –
Vitruvius, Frontinus, Celsus, Pliny – Geminus, Strabo,
Ptolemy, Galen*

★

THE GRAECO-ROMAN AGE

WHILE the first Ptolemies were consolidating their empire
over Egypt an event of even greater importance had been
taking place in the west. The city of Rome had conquered
and organized Italy. The Italian communities were separated
from their conquerors by no great cultural or racial gap, and
the Romans found in the sturdy and numerous peasantry of
Italy a vast reservoir of military power. In this they were
more fortunately placed than the Ptolemies at Alexandria
who found it necessary to hold Egypt with an army at first
exclusively and always mainly Greek, or than the Phoenicians
at Carthage whose imperial ambitions were insecurely based
on mercenary armies enrolled from Berber tribesmen. Rome
and Italy were capable of a degree of unity impossible to
Alexandria and Egypt, or to Carthage and Africa. This was
the condition of Rome's becoming mistress of the world.

The strength of the new power was soon revealed. Pyrrhus
of Epirus, who aspired to the role of Alexander in the west,
led an army into Italy expecting an easy conquest. If he had
been able to subdue Rome he would have led the Greeks of
Magna Graecia against Carthage. His career was checked
before it had well begun by his decisive defeat by the
Romans in 275 B.C. Hegemony, first over the Italian Greeks,
then over the Sicilian Greeks, passed to Rome. Partnership
between Romans and Greeks had begun. Before the close of

the third century Carthage had been humbled in two long
and hard-fought wars. The opening of the second century
found the Romans moving east, and before the century had
run half its course the successors of Alexander in the east,
the Antigonids of Macedon and the Seleucids of Syria, had
been crushed. The Greek cities both of Asia Minor and of
the mainland had taken their place with those of southern
Italy and Sicily as ornaments of the Roman world. Only
Egypt remained. It was incorporated into the Empire by
Augustus.

These were the events which produced the cultural epoch
known as the Graeco-Roman Age. The Romans who, with
superb political skill, effected the unification of Italy, were
not a cultured people. They had no literature. Their
language, which, save for a few garrisons and colonies, was
confined to the district of Latium in the neighbourhood of
Rome and the Tiber, had indeed begun to be fashioned into
an idiom fit for political debate and decision but had never
been used for the expression of philosophical or scientific
ideas. But now the Romans found themselves masters successively of the Greek cities of Magna Graecia, of Greece
proper, and of Ionia. They who spoke the undeveloped
language of a small district of Italy found themselves politi-
cally masters of the Mediterranean which culturally was a
Greek lake. They who previous to their contacts with the
Greeks had no literature found themselves masters of a
people whose literature was five or six centuries old and had
already become the subject of sophisticated and scholarly
appreciation. Inevitably their boys began to be schooled by
Greek grammarians and their statesmen by Greek politi-
cians. Their entertainments, their learned professions, were
in the hands of Greeks. Their nascent literature was modelled
on the Greek. The culture of the Roman world became
bilingual. Make yourself expert in the two tongues, advised

Ovid in his *Art of Love*, if you wish not to bore your mistress. The advice was found valid and acted upon in other spheres. Every Roman who wanted to be at all cultured had to learn Greek, every Greek who wanted to sell his culture had to learn the language of his Roman master. It was the Greeks who had the knowledge, but the Roman mastery was not a mere political fact. It had its meaning also in the spiritual sphere. Rome had succeeded where Greece had failed and on the Romans rested the responsibility of power. Roman literature is not a mere imitation of Greek but the expression of a new era. The Romans formed themselves mentally by their effort to digest an alien culture, but they chose to digest it for their own ends. Roman culture, if less original, has a new complexity and a new maturity. Cicero imitates Plato, but discourses of actual government rather than of ideal justice. Lucretius sets up his rest in the Garden of Epicurus, but addresses the Senate and the People therefrom. Virgil follows Hesiod over his farm, but does so at an Emperor's nod. Tacitus traces the decline of oratory, but reads in it the story of a political revolution. This new consciousness which characterizes the literature of Rome corresponds to a new social and political configuration of the world. A vast area of the world, through the building of roads, the improvement of ships and harbours, the movements of armies, the invention of new political forms, and the possession of a common language, had become one. The *oikoumene*, the inhabited world, was a more complicated organism than any city state, and in the mind of its Roman masters and their Greek teachers the problems of its management begin dimly to take shape. For the most part they seem so overwhelming that man resigns himself to mysticism, to cynicism, to fate, the stars, the gods, the emperor. The companion picture to the growth of science at this time is the story of the spread of oriental religions and the relapse of the various philosophies into schools of resignation. But in the books and writers we shall now discuss we shall see some refreshing evidence of the capacity of man to take his destiny into his own hands.

BILINGUAL CULTURE : THE GRAMMARIAN, THE ENCYCLOPAEDIST, THE TRANSLATOR

The bilingualism of the Graeco-Roman world means that from about 100 B.C. European science had two tongues, but the work was unequally distributed between them. The work of advancing the now traditional branches of science continues to be done in Greek. In Latin was done a work of assimilation and adaptation to Roman needs, which involved criticism, selection and organization and produced a few masterpieces of a new type.

One consequence of this relation of Roman to Greek science is that grammar, one of the last sciences to be constituted by the Greeks, was the first in which the Romans achieved mastery. It remains one of their great achievements. The Romans, studying in Greek and writing in Latin, became grammar conscious in a new way. The Greeks had become grammar conscious through the necessity of interpreting old writers in their own tongue. It was the need of studying a second tongue that made the Romans grammarians. Forced by their national pride not to become culturally a Greek province and engaged in the effort to transfer into Latin speech the literary and scientific culture of Greece, they found that the first Greek science they had urgent need to adopt, and to adapt, was grammar. Their first great grammarian was Lucius Aelius Stilo (about 154-74 B.C.) who studied in Rhodes at a time when Dionysius Thrax, long expelled from Alexandria, was resident there. Stilo's greatest pupil was Marcus Terentius Varro (116-27 B.C.), author of twenty-five books on the Latin language of which we still possess six. The list of Roman grammarians is long and there is no reason to give it here. But, coming to the end of a great succession, we may mention two names. Donatus, who lived in the middle of the fourth century A.D., was so famous that, like Euclid, he gave his name to his subject. In the late Middle Ages a grammar was called a Donat. Still greater than he was Priscian whose *Institutiones Grammaticae* in eighteen books, which appeared about A.D. 500, is the most famous of all ancient grammars. In spite of its formidable length (it is about as long as the modern Latin grammar of Madvig) its popularity was once so great that no library in Europe was without a copy and it survives to this day in about one thousand MSS. The debt of culture to the Roman grammarians is immense.

Linguistic phenomena have not proved the easiest sort of material for science to analyse. An example of the way the Roman grammarians set about it may be welcome. Thus in his *Art of Grammar* Donatus begins by defining *Vox*, or Voice. 'Voice is air in vibration which is perceptible to hearing. Every vocal utterance is either articulate or confused. By articulate I mean that which can be expressed in letters, by confused that which cannot be written.' Priscian evidently feels this to be on the right lines but inadequate, and at the beginning of his Bk. I offers a more extensive analysis. 'The philosophers define voice as a small quantity of air in vibration, or its effect on the ears. The first definition is of substance, the second of accident. For hearing is something that happens to voice. There are four kinds of vocal utterance : articulate, inarticulate, literate and illiterate. Articulate is that which is accompanied with meaning by the speaker. Inarticulate is accompanied by no meaning. Literate is what can be written, illiterate what cannot. An example of articulate literate utterance is "Arms and the man I sing". Articulate illiterate utterances are groans, whistles, sighs. They have an intended meaning but cannot be written down. Inarticulate literate utterances are such as "coax" or "cra". They can be written down but they mean nothing. Inarticulate illiterate vocal utterances, which neither convey a meaning nor can be written down, are chattering, or mooing.'

Varro, whom we mentioned a moment ago, is not only the author of the first Latin grammar which is extant in large part. He is also for us the best early example of an encyclopaedist. His grammar was but the first part of a great work which included also logic, rhetoric, geometry, arithmetic, astronomy, music, medicine and architecture. The Romans had looked at first with a somewhat jaundiced eye on the culture of the Greeks. When we come to Varro we can say that they had made up their minds that it was indispensable and resolved to assimilate it. It is also clear that the form in which they assimilated it had very durable qualities. Varro's conception of an encyclopaedia of knowledge lasted through the Middle Ages and down into modern times. Only modern developments of the natural and historical sciences have made it date.

CICERO AND LUCRETIUS

But the writings of the grammarians and encyclopaedists, though by no means to be despised, pale into insignificance beside the achievement of the two men who, by endowing the work of selection, criticism and reorganization with the brilliance of their own genius, did more than any others to bring it about that Latin should become the mediator to Western Europe of the wisdom of the Greeks. Cicero and Lucretius, vastly different as their spiritual and mental endowments were, both left behind them imperishable masterpieces which, if we exclude the plays of Plautus and Terence, are the first monuments of Latin genius which still exert a living influence on the thought and style of the modern world. What is the secret of the influence of these two men?

In the last century of the pagan era two Greek schools of thought, the Stoic and the Epicurean, contended for the allegiance of Romans who aspired to philosophy. Of sects other than these the most important were the various Socratic schools; but they were so much closer to the Porch than to the Garden that it might fairly be said that the one real division was between the followers of Epicurus and the rest. The Epicureans, like their rivals, taught belief in the gods. But they limited the sphere of action of their gods to the inner personal life, teaching that good men have communion with the blessed gods while bad men terrify themselves by imaginary fears of them. They differed sharply from the other schools by banishing the gods from nature and from society. Their gods neither made worlds nor ruled them, had not taught men the rudiments of civilization nor guided them to its refinements, were not guardians of property or public morality, dropped no thunderbolts on the rebel or the perjuror. It followed that in a city like Rome, which had been founded and guided by gods, where no public act was done without consulting the will of the gods, where the gods powerfully assisted in the maintenance of order, Epicureans were hardly fit for public life. On the other hand wherever men studied nature, not as a manifestation of the mind of a benevolent providence, but as a non-human environment by the control of which men had laid the foundations of civilized life; wherever men studied history, not to trace in it the mysterious intentions of the gods, but as a record of the trials and errors of mankind; wherever men thought of society as a sphere in which man by the exercise of his political or technical inventiveness might improve his conditions of life; wherever human nature was studied as a basis for a rational control of the instinctive life; there the teachings of Epicurus was likely to be at the root of it. Such was the philosophical atmosphere of the world into which Cicero and Lucretius were born and in which they grew up to be the champions of such opposite points of view.

Cicero was a public man, and though he numbered many Epicureans among his private friends, in his published writings he had no good to say of their sect. His philosophy was a blend of Platonism and Stoicism. He inclined to the metaphysics of Plato and the ethics of Zeno, or rather to refinements of their teaching introduced by later generations in these schools. Nobody regards him as an original thinker nor am I among those who feel his borrowed opinions to have been held with such sincerity as to endow them with the interest of being the creed of a great man. He hardly set this value on them himself. All the same he merits our attention and our admiration. The author in politics of a *Republic* and a *Laws*, in which the teaching of Plato is applied to the history and the problems of the Roman state; in metaphysics of the *Academica* and the *Tusculan Disputations*, in which words and formulae are devised for the expression in Latin of the fundamental problems of traditional philosophy; in ethics of the *De Finibus* and the *De Officiis*, where the same is done for the domain of conduct; he gave so many examples of an adroit exploitation of Greek sources to produce new Latin works, and of an adroit solution of the innumerable problems that beset the translator, that he must take a high place in the history of the transmission of ideas. Perfunctory as his thinking is, there is charm in the eager response of his mind to the impact of new ideas, in the virtuosity with which he endows his undeveloped native idiom with all the qualities necessary to express the thought of a Plato or a Xenophon, in the inexhaustible mastery of words. He was a great man of letters as well as an orator and a politician, and the stamp of his personality rests on all his work. In that field also in which philosophy borders upon science he has left work of the greatest interest, namely, a version, extant in part, of the *Timaeus* of Plato, and a more or less original work *On Divination*, where for once he has written with sincerity and passion. This is a treatise in two books in dialogue form. In the first he assigns to his brother Quintus the task of defending the ancient practice of consulting the will of the gods by augury, haruspicy, astrology, and all the other devices known to antiquity. In the second he reserves for himself the more grateful, and the hardier, task of discrediting the whole conception. This he does with point and spirit, not hesitating even to conclude with the expression of his belief that 'he would be rendering a great service to himself and his country if he could tear this superstition up by the roots'. This revolutionary impulse in Cicero, directed against proved and established institutions which he had elsewhere defended for their utility, is a surprising phenomenon.

It is the attack on superstition which does most to bring Cicero close, if only for a moment, to his contemporary Lucretius. Lucretius was a follower of Epicurus, that is to say a member of that school which, almost alone at this time, fought to rid nature and history of the arbitrary interference of supernatural forces. His work is our best example of the capacity of Roman writers to assimilate a mass of Greek learning and create a new organic whole out of it. The basis of the philosophy of Epicurus was the atomism of Leucippus and Democritus. But atomism had come under the fire of the Socratic schools and the task of Epicurus had been to restate the atomistic position in the light of the criticism of Plato and Aristotle. Atomism as reconstructed by Epicurus was the philosophy Lucretius undertook to expound to his Roman audience; but there is no doubt that he did not confine himself to the three hundred scrolls of his master but made an independent study of the Presocratics, notably Heraclitus, Anaxagoras and Democritus. He had studied also the Hippocratic writings and Thucydides, material from whom he uses in his sixth book; and the mistakes he has made in interpreting them are proof, if any were needed, that these were not easy studies. He directly criticizes opinions of Plato, though without mention of his name. Homer, Aeschylus, Euripides have also left their imprint on his work. Such was the Greek material he had studied and digested.

One other Greek source remains to be mentioned, the philosophical poem *On Nature* by the Presocratic philosopher, Empedocles of Acragas. Lucretius followed his example in choosing verse as the medium for the exposition of his theme. The verse form has been an obstacle to some students of Lucretius. Many agree with Shelley's protest 'Didactic poetry is my abhorrence. Nothing can be equally well expressed in prose that is not tedious and supererogatory in verse.' It is a superficial opinion. Half the best poetry of antiquity is didactic. When an author has a great subject to expound, the importance of which he feels deeply, which stirs his emotions as well as his thought, which haunts his imagination as well as his reason, which he plans to bring home to the heart as well as the mind of his hearers, poetry has many resources of eloquence by which to engage the attention, rouse the interest and impress the memory. These qualities Lucretius found in Empedocles and he was glad to have a poet as his model, for the Latin language of his day was much better developed in verse than in prose. In philosophic verse he already had a Latin predecessor in Ennius. Philosophic prose was only being created in his own day, partly by Epicureans whose works are lost but mainly by Cicero.

A contemporary situation invested atomism in the mind

of Lucretius with the attributes of an evangel. According to him the world of living men groaned under a burden of fear – fear of going under in the grinding struggle for existence, fear of disaster overtaking them as punishment for sin, fear of death, fear of punishment in the afterlife. The first of these fears Lucretius sought to exorcize by a doctrine of philosophic anarchism. He thought if men would be content to live the simple life there could not fail to be enough for all. 'A frugal life with a heart at rest is great riches, and never is there lack of a little', he sings – sufficient proof, if any were wanted, that he himself enjoyed reasonable security and comfort. To the other fears he had given more serious thought. These fears, natural to men, especially to ignorant men, were also inculcated in the masses for reasons of state. Polybius, Varro, Cicero, all advocate the use of superstition for the purpose of policing the mob. Having elsewhere [1] reported their opinions I offer here a quotation from another source. Strabo, writing about 30 B.C., says: 'Poets were not alone in giving currency to myths. Long before the poets, cities and their lawgivers had sanctioned them as a useful expedient. They had some insight into the emotional nature of the rational animal. Illiterate and un-educated men, they argued, are no better than children and, like them, are fond of stories. When, through descriptive narratives or other forms of representational art, they learn how terrible are divine punishments and threats, they are deterred from their evil courses. No philosopher by means of a reasoned exhortation can move a crowd of women or any random mob to reverence, piety and faith. He needs to play upon their superstition also, and this cannot be done without myths and marvels. It was, then, as bugbears to scare the simple-minded that founders of states gave their sanction to these things. This is the function of mythology

1. See my *Science and Politics in the Ancient World*.

and it accordingly came to have its recognized place in the ancient plan of civil society as well as in the explanations of the nature of reality.' (*Geography*, I, 2, 8.)[2]

Epicureanism for Lucretius meant war to the knife on this view of the plan of civil society. In the opening of his poem he proclaims that the philosophy he propounds is able to give man victory over *religio*, that is to say, the official mythology. He warns those who wish to follow him that their path will not be altogether smooth, for they will have to contend against the opposition of men whom he calls *vates* or seers, who will play upon their fears of what may happen after death to unbelievers. A true philosophy of nature is the weapon with which he fights these fears. Twice in his poem he declares that the old Greek natural philosophers, and not the oracle of Apollo at Delphi, ought to be revered as the fountainhead of truth. Such was the situation Lucretius sought to influence, and such was his message.

His poem is unfinished, but the plan of the six extant books which he brought near completion is both comprehensive and clear. His first two books are concerned with the fundamental principles of the atomic explanation of the nature of the physical world. The next two books treat of man, the first expounding the nature of the soul and the way in which it is connected with the body, giving proofs of the mortality of the soul, and attempting to exorcize the fear of death ; the second dealing with sensation, thought, and biological functions. Book five deals with our world and its history, describing its formation, the nature and motions of the heavenly bodies, and the beginnings of life and of civilization ; book six with meteorological phenomena, curious happenings on earth, pestilences in general and in particular the great plague at Athens during the Peloponnesian War. In

2. Strabo claims that the history and science of a later date was better, but adds at once that it was only for the *élite*.

no other single work in the whole of antiquity, and I think I might add in the modern world either, is there to be found a comparable effort to muster all the phenomena of nature and history as joint witnesses to a unified view of things. The book is truly encyclopaedic but is the least possible like an encyclopaedia, for every item of information it contains is but part of a single argument. An intense intellectual excitement pervades every part and is even heightened by the unfinished state of the work. One feels that Lucretius must have died like Buckle, exclaiming 'My book, my book!'

Of the inexhaustible variety of matter contained in these teeming pages, one topic – the sketch of the origin and progress of civilization, which occupies the second half of book five – most concerns us here. In our first volume (pp. 73–7) we gave special emphasis, as the true culmination of Presocratic science, to a brief sketch of civilization taken from Democritus[3] and preserved for us by the historian Diodorus. Lucretius, the contemporary of Diodorus, gives us, in some seven hundred lines, what looks like an elaboration of the same sketch made in the Epicurean school. In its elimination of the action of providence and its search for intelligible causes in the domain of human history it constitutes perhaps the ripest contribution of antiquity to the science of the modern world. Accordingly we shall summarize it at some length.

The earth, the poet tells us, brought forth first vegetable life and then living things. Of these the first were birds which hatched from eggs, next came animals born out of wombs rooted in the earth. Earth fed and clothed them and tempered the climate to them. But in time she grew old and

3. The probability of the ascription of this passage to Democritus is strengthened by the latest research. See *On the Pre-history in Diodorus* by Gregory Vlastos. *American Journal of Philology*, Vol. LXVII, 1 (Jan., 1946).

ceased to bear, and living things began to propagate themselves. Before she ceased bearing earth produced many monsters now extinct. In fact all species that could not find their food or propagate their kind or protect themselves or, in the last resort, win man's protection in return for their services to him, died out.

Primitive man was hardier than men now and longer-lived. He was not a producer but a food-gatherer. He did not have fire, clothing or houses, but dwelt in woods or mountain caves and mated promiscuously. The more dangerous wild beasts he avoided, others he hunted with sticks and stones. Civilization began after man got fire, skin-clothing and huts. Man and wife then began to mate permanently and know the tenderness of parenthood. Civil society began in friendship and compacts with neighbours. Language was a product of society. It could not have been invented by one man and imparted by him to his fellows ; but, just as dogs, horses and birds express the variety of their emotions by various sounds, so did man use different sounds to designate different things until by convention language was established.

The knowledge of fire came either through a conflagration caused by lightning or the ignition of branches of trees rubbed together by the wind. The sun taught men to cook. Then gradually those whose technical inventiveness gave them the lead emerged as kings and built cities, each with a citadel as a stronghold and refuge for himself. The kings parcelled out flocks and fields to their subjects, at first according to their personal qualities of mind or body. But the invention of money and the growth of property completely altered the conditions of life. Riches now became more important than personal worth, and, in the envious and ambitious society that resulted, monarchy was overthrown and anarchy prevailed. Out of this anarchy emerged constitutional government. Magistrates were appointed, laws promulgated, and crime was held in check by legal sanctions. The poet next turns to religion. What is the cause of its universal prevalence? It is found everywhere among great peoples. It has filled the cities with altars and led to annual celebrations which strike shuddering dread into mortal men, who then spread the evil and erect new temples over the whole world with new crowds of worshippers.[4] It results from a confusion of ideas among those who have not a true philosophy of nature. Men, waking and sleeping, see the gods in all their glory and (rightly) ascribe to them blessedness and immortality. They behold also the phenomena of the heavens, majestic, regular, and incomprehensible. So they imagine that the gods dwell in heaven and guide all these celestial happenings by their will. 'O hapless race of men, when they charged the gods with such acts and imagined them at the same time capable of bitter wrath! What groanings did they beget for themselves, what wounds for us, what tears for our children's children! No act is it of piety to be often seen with veiled head to turn towards a stone and approach every altar and fall prostrate on the ground and spread out the palms before the statues of the gods and sprinkle the altars with much blood of beasts and link vow on vow, but rather to be able to look on all things with a mind at peace.'

Man's first lessons in metallurgy were given when forest fires melted gold, silver, lead, copper and iron and suggested to him the forging of weapons and instruments. Previous to his knowledge of metals man's weapons and implements had been hands, nails, teeth, stones, branches torn from trees, and flame and fire when once they were known. Horses were ridden before war-chariots were invented. The Cartha-

4. Compare the account given above (pp. 56ff.) of the spread of the cult of Serapis.

ginians introduced elephants into war. Garments tied to-gether came before woven raiment, for the loom could not be constructed before the invention of iron. Men were the first weavers, but later abandoned this craft to women and went to work in the fields. Sowing and grafting were lessons taught by nature, and the gradual extension of tilth drove the woods farther up the hills and gave us the smiling land-scapes we now enjoy. Music was first an imitation of bird-song and whistling winds. Sun and moon taught man the regularity of the seasons and to adapt his work to them. Walled towns, navigation, treaties, and the celebration of great deeds in song all followed in due course. 'Ships and tillage, walls, laws, arms, roads, dress and all such like things, all the prizes, all the elegancies too of life without exception, poems, pictures and the chiselling of fine-wrought statues, all these things practice together with the acquired knowledge of the untiring mind taught men by slow degrees as they advanced on the way step by step. Thus time by degrees brings each several thing forth before men's eyes and reason raises it up into the borders of light ; for things must be brought to light one after another and in due order in the different arts, until these have reached their highest point of development.'

Many of the principal features of this sketch of human progress have contributed, and are perhaps even still capable of contributing, to the growth of the science of history. We may note the fundamental importance attached to the achievement of the great technical inventions. Much history still remains to be rewritten in the light of this conception. We may note, too, the conception of science as an imitation of nature by which man learns to control the natural environ-ment in his own interest. Very remarkable is the sense shown of the dependence of the intellectual and moral life of man on his external circumstances. Control of fire, he teaches, made man a social animal: society gave birth to language. Rudimentary architecture allowed a mating couple to share a hut; conjugal and parental love began to develop. But the process has its inherent contradictions. Fire, which makes civilization possible, weakens man physically. Or again, the invention of property and money throws society into confusion. Religion is seen to contain elements of truth, but to be tragically mingled with error arising from ignorance of science, and cruelly exploited by the rulers in order to maintain their power (compare Bk. I, 102–17). Finally there is the realization that history follows laws, in so far as 'things must be brought to light one after another and in due order in the different arts'.

The poem of Lucretius is sometimes described as a versified text-book of atomic physics. Those who hold this view of it will think that we have misrepresented it in concentrating attention on that portion of it devoted to the sketch of human progress. But our emphasis is not wrong. The poem is essentially an analysis of human history and society which, in the mind of Lucretius, were continuous with the history of the physical universe. The main theme of the poem is the social and psychological consequence of man's action upon nature, of man's knowledge or ignorance of nature, of man's lies about nature.

The poem stands in a strange isolation in Roman literature. It may be said to record the opinions of the defeated party in ancient philosophy. Its fundamental ideas, surviving from the Presocratic schools, proved incompatible with the development, or decline, of ancient society. Virgil as a youth deeply studied Epicurus and always continued to love the poem of Lucretius, but he discarded the views of these men in the process of becoming the poet of the Augustan reform. Providence then became his theme. Human history turned on miracles and oracles. The fundamental arts of life were represented as divine revelations. The hardness of man's lot was explained as a careful provision of Jove for his moral and intellectual training. But though the thoughts of Lucretius were drawn from Ionia and bore some characteristics of an age when men still had confidence in their ability to shape their own destiny, it must not be thought that he shared this confidence. He lived in a declining civilization when all prospect of fundamental improvement lay below the horizon of thought. He believed that the world was worn out and would soon break up, sending its individual atoms raining through space. His thoughts were the echo of a nobler dead world. In his shame at the world of political contrivance in which he lived his favourite epithets for the old materialist philosophers were 'serious' and 'holy'.

VITRUVIUS

Meanwhile the world, such as it was, continued to exist, and the Romans continued to take over from the Greeks not only their philosophy but their more practical arts. The Roman work of selection and reorganization of Greek sources is particularly well represented in the treatise *On Architecture* of Vitruvius. This book, written for Octavian some time before he assumed the title of Augustus in 27 B.C., is much more comprehensive than its title suggests. Its ten books deal with the general principles of architecture, the evolution of building and the use of materials, the various temple styles (Ionic, Doric and Corinthian), public buildings (theatres, baths and harbours), town and country houses, interior decoration, water-supply, sun-dials and clocks, mechanical and military engineering. It is probable that such a comprehensive and orderly work was a novelty. In the Preface to his sixth book he mentions (par. 12) a dozen Greek architects who had written descriptions of masterpieces of their own design and construction, and (par. 14) a dozen names of Greek writers on mechanics. It is certain that this is not an empty display of erudition. Some or all of their works he had studied and assimilated, if not perfectly, then to the best of his ability. But the intention, and the ability, to reduce this varied and difficult material in a foreign tongue into a practical manual written 'for the foreman and the works manager' were his own. The architect, complains Briggs, is missing from history. We have the names and boastful epitaphs of Egyptian architects, not even the names of the Mesopotamian, and nothing from the Hebrews or the Cretans. Many names of Greek architects are known but their works are lost. For us the literature of architecture begins with Vitruvius, and this is likely to be due not to an historical accident but to the merit, that is to say the comprehensiveness, orderliness and practical usefulness, of his work.

One of the charms of Vitruvius is that he gives us many autobiographical glimpses of his own simple and sterling character. He recalls (Bk. VI, Intro. 3 and 4) that while the laws of all the Greeks required that children should maintain their parents, the Athenians added the proviso that this should only apply to parents who had educated their children in some art or craft. 'Hence', he adds, 'I am very much obliged to my parents for their approval of this Athenian law. They saw to it that I should be taught an art, and one moreover that cannot be perfectly acquired without an extensive training in the liberal arts. Thanks to my parents and my teachers I obtained a wide education, am able to appreciate art and literature, and am myself an author.' The breadth of his interests and knowledge and the fineness of his taste are apparent in his work, which is an important source for our knowledge of ancient science and civilization.

Sometimes the opinions of Vitruvius are to be read between the lines. Thus (Bk. 1, 2, 7) he recommends selecting 'very healthy neighbourhoods with suitable springs of water in places where fanes are to be built, particularly in the case of those to Aesculapius and to Health, gods by whose healing powers great numbers of the sick are apparently cured. For when their diseased bodies are transferred from an unhealthy to a healthy spot, and treated with water from health-giving springs, they will the more speedily grow well. The result will be that the divinity will stand in higher esteem and find his dignity increased, all owing to the nature of his site.' A similar discreet scepticism is revealed in another passage (IX, 6, 2) where astrology, an almost universal superstition at this time, is politely cold-shouldered.

We have described in our last chapter the firmness with which Greek science at its height, with Theophrastus, Strato and Archimedes, had grasped the idea of experiment. Vitruvius will illustrate for us both the survival of the idea and the insecurity with which it was held. Among the best-known passages of his book is the Introduction to Bk. IX where he describes the experiment which led Archimedes to the discovery of specific gravity. Elsewhere (Bk. VII, 8, 3) he himself recommends a repetition of this experiment with quicksilver. A stone weighing one hundred pounds will float upon quicksilver, a scruple of gold will sink in it. 'Hence the certain inference that the gravity of a substance depends not on the amount of the weight but on the nature of the substance.' But an appeal to experiment was more often made simply as an illustration of an already formed opinion, which might be false. Bk. I, 6, 1 and 2 offers a good example. Vitruvius is here engaged in a sensible discussion of the proper siting of a town in relation to the prevailing wind. Mytilene, he says, is magnificently built but not sensibly sited. Here ' when the South wind blows men fall ill, when the North-west blows they cough, when the North blows they are restored to health but the cold is such that they cannot stand in the alleys and streets'. These excellent observations lead him on to a disquisition on the nature of wind. He does not know that wind is simply air in motion but supposes it to be an addition to the existing air. 'It is produced when heat meets moisture, the rush of heat generating a mighty current of air. That this is a fact we may learn from bronze eolipiles, a technical invention sufficing to bring to light a divine truth hidden in the laws of the heavens. Eolipiles are hollow bronze balls with a small opening through which water is poured in. If they are set before a fire, not a breath issues from them before they get warm, but, as soon as they begin to boil, out comes a strong blast caused by the heat. From this small and easily performed experiment we may judge of the mighty and wonderful laws of the heavens and the nature of winds.' It is worth noting that this 'experimentally' established *untruth* persisted into quite modern times. In the eighteenth century the enlightened traveller, ten Rhyne, quite a reputable scientist in his day, detected in the cloud over Table Mountain at the Cape of Good Hope the source from which the mighty south-easter was being 'poured into' the atmosphere.

The 'experiment' with the eolipile is really not an experiment at all but an argument from analogy. A still more extraordinary misuse of this type of argument is found in Bk. VI, 1, 5 and 6. Vitruvius accepts without question an opinion, current in his day, that northern peoples have deep voices and southern peoples shrill ones. He imagines this human phenomenon to derive its explanation from the very structure of the universe. The Greeks were familiar with a triangular stringed instrument called the sambuca. A diagram made up of the circle of the horizon, a diameter bisecting it from north to south, and an oblique line drawn up

from the south point to the Pole star 'clearly shows that
the world has a triangular shape like the sambuca'. If
we imagine the longest string of this world instrument
to be dropped from the Pole star to the diameter at the
horizon and the rest of the parallel strings to grow pro-
gressively shorter towards the south, we can understand
by analogy why the human voice becomes deeper as we go
north!

Two more passages may be referred to in illustration of
the scope of this book, which, apart from its merits as a
manual of architecture, is rich in material for historians of
almost every branch of ancient science. Bk. II, 1, 1–8 gives a
sketch of the cultural development of early man bringing
in the discovery of fire, the origin of speech, and in particular the evolution of architecture. The chapter is important
for the early history of anthropology. Allusion is made to
contemporary building practice in Gaul, Spain, Portugal and
Aquitaine ; and the architecture of the Colchians in Pontus,
'where there are forests in plenty', is contrasted with that
of the Phrygians, 'who live in an open country, have no
forests and consequently lack timber'. In a fine passage of
the same book (chapter 9), where the information is derived
from Theophrastus, the suitability of various types of timber
for building is discussed. From this we quote a few sentences
about the preparation of seasoned timber. 'In felling a tree
cut the trunk into the very heart and leave it standing so that
the sap may drain completely out. This lets the useless liquid
run out through the sapwood and the quality of the wood
will not be corrupted. Then and not till then let the tree be
felled and it will be in the highest state of usefulness.' It is
probable that this practice is very old. In the *Odyssey* Calypso
leads Odysseus to a place where he can *cut down* seasoned
timber for his raft. The idea of seasoned timber still standing
was so strange to Samuel Butler that he took this as one

example of that ignorance of men's affairs which proved that the *Odyssey* was written by a woman.

Evidence of Vitruvius's competence in matters of artistic taste will be found in his chapter on The Decadence of Fresco Painting (Bk. VII, 5). Its fine sensibility is not at all out of harmony with the unpretentious and practical character of his work.

FRONTINUS

Practicality carried even to excess distinguishes the work on the aqueducts of Rome by Frontinus. Sextus Julius Frontinus was an experienced man of affairs, used to the highest responsibilities. After his first consulship he was despatched as Governor to Britain where he triumphed over the warlike Silures and their still more intractable habitat. In A.D. 97 he was made commissioner of waterworks by Nerva. He was already an experienced author—his *Art of War*, which is lost, and his *Stratagems*, which we have, must have been written between his return from Britain and his appointment as water commissioner—and when he had thoroughly familiarized himself with all the knowledge relevant to his new duties, in order, as he said, to make himself independent of the advice of subordinates, and when the success of his administration was clear, he digested the results of his studies and his practice into his brief and brilliant treatise on the water-supply of Rome. The absence of adornment is part of the merit of his work. His facts speak for themselves. For 441 years from the foundation of the City, he tells us, the Romans were satisfied with such waters as they drew from the Tiber. Now, however, the following aqueducts convey water from near and far to the City : The Appian, the Old Anio, the Marcia, the Tepula, the Julia, the Virgo, the Alsietina or Augusta, the Claudia and the New Anio. There follow essential details: the lengths of the aqueducts, interesting features like the settling reservoir of the New Anio, the quality of the various sources of supply (Augusta was unwholesome and unfit for drinking), an account of the secret plundering of Julia by branch pipes and how these pipes were detected and destroyed. After a few such paragraphs, packed with telling detail, he permits himself a curt reflection. 'With such an array of indispensable structures carrying so many waters compare, if you will, the idle pyramids or the useless though famous works of the Greeks.' It is a memorable comment, though a Vitruvius would not have expressed himself with so little sympathy about the temples of the Greeks.

It is probable, as his latest editor suggests, that the composition of Frontinus's book was dictated by a political as well as an administrative purpose. It may have been a blow in support of Nerva's policy of weakening the power of freedmen in the administration and strengthening the power of the senate. Whatever its purpose its testimony to the public spirit and ability of its author remains the same. Rarely in any ancient writing does one have the feeling of being introduced with such competence into a branch of applied science. We read of the plans of the aqueducts drawn to assist calculations of the cost of upkeep, of the builders, dates, sources, lengths and elevations of the aqueducts, of the size of the supply, the number of reservoirs, the quality of the water, and the purpose for which it was supplied. Special attention is paid to the ajutages, the nozzles which assisted in the calculation of delivery. We hear of ajutages of wrong sizes and of ajutages which did not bear the official stamp. Frontinus is very sensible of the difficulty of calculation, but he dryly adds, 'when less is found in the delivery ajutages and more in the receiving ajutages, it is obvious that there is not error but fraud'. He was determined not to stand for either. *De*

Aquis is a work of applied science only and has less claim to appear in a history of science than the *De Architectura* which, though strictly a work of applied science, is rich in reflections on the theory on which the practice is based. Yet the sense of public service is becoming part of the modern conception of science, and it is difficult to find a better example of science in the service of the public than is supplied by Frontinus. His sense of the benefits it can confer upon mankind is beautifully expressed in the direct and simple statement with which we conclude our account of his book. 'The effect of this care displayed by the Emperor Nerva, most public-spirited of rulers, is felt from day to day increasingly and will be still more felt in the health of the City ... Not even the waste water is lost. The appearance of the City is clean and altered. The air is purer, and the causes of the unwholesome atmosphere which gave the City so bad a name with earlier generations are now removed.'

CELSUS

Some historians of science have seen in Cornelius Celsus, who has left us the best general treatise on medicine of all the ancients, a supreme example of the Roman ability to digest and organize the science created by the Greeks. This is a mistake. The merits of Celsus have been fully acknowledged when we recognize in him an admirable stylist. The work *On Medicine* which has come down to us under his name is a translation, with adaptations consisting chiefly of omissions, of the work of a Sicilian called Titus Aufidius who wrote in Greek. Greek medicine had become fashionable in Rome in the first half of the first century B.C. after the arrival in the capital of the attractive and energetic Bithynian physician Asclepiades. He had a number of distinguished pupils and among these was Aufidius, the writer whose work Celsus selected for translation. The debt of Celsus to Aufidius was obscure until it was revealed by the patient analysis of his modern editor, F. Marx. Samuel Butler somewhere observes that an author is apt to omit acknowledgments to an authority to whom he is very heavily indebted. This cynical remark, alas, applies to Celsus. He mentions Asclepiades and his disciple Themison. Aufidius he does not mention. Thus he managed to run away with the reputation of having himself arranged the excellent treatise which bears his name. It would have been better for his fame if he had been satisfied to be known as a translator and stylist. Here his achievement is unassailable. He is, as Sir Clifford Allbutt has called him, the creator of scientific Latin.

Roman writers who refer to Celsus describe him as a man of only moderate talent. Doubtless they knew that he was only a translator. Aufidius, however, had genius of a rare quality. He had a real intellectual style. His superiority shows itself in his grasp of the history of his subject, as well as of its present potentialities, in his adherence to the noblest traditions of practice, in the scrupulosity with which he gives credit to older physicians where credit is due, and in his readiness where necessary to criticize his contemporaries. His fairness and his fearlessness both spring from his conscious worth. He had a contribution to make to medical practice of great moment, greater than may appear at first sight. He was unwilling to regard any rule as of universal application. Recognizing the efficacy of bleedings, purgings, vomiting and massage, he insisted that the time and degree of their employment must always be determined by the state of the patient's strength. This meant an immense emphasis on the importance of first-hand clinical observation. His patients were his books. He studied sick men, not diseases. He was in the line of the great healers. In his humanity, his intellectual integrity and his respect for his art he points back towards Hippocrates and forward to the great clinicians of modern times. These qualities we shall illustrate by a quotation.

This is a fairly complete description of fevers. The methods of treatment vary according to the authorities. Asclepiades says it is the business of the doctor to effect a safe, speedy and pleasant cure. That is much to be desired, but too much haste and too much pleasure are both apt to be dangerous. We shall have to consider at each stage of the treatment how to secure the maximum of safety, speed and pleasure while restoring the patient to his original state of health.

The first point to be settled is the treatment of the patient during the first days. The old doctors strove to promote concoction by the giving of certain medicines, their particular dread being the opposite state of crudity. Next they tried by frequent evacuations to get rid of what seemed to be the noxious matter. Asclepiades did away with medicines. He did not employ evacuations so frequently, but still in every disease. His claim was that he used the fever itself as the chief cure for the fever. He thought the strength of the patient ought to be undermined by strong light, vigils and thirst. He would not even let the face be washed on the first day. The more mistaken they who supposed his regimen to have been pleasant throughout! The fact is that in the last days he pandered to the fancies of the patient, in the first he showed himself in the guise of a torturer. My own opinion is that medicinal draughts and evacuations should be employed only rarely, nor should their purpose be supposed to be to undermine the strength of the patient, since the chief danger is from weakness. Any superabundance of matter should therefore be reduced, but this is naturally digested if nothing new is added. There should thus be abstinence from food in the first days. The patient, unless he is weak, should be kept in the light by day. Thirst and sleep should be controlled in such a way as to secure wakefulness by day. At night, if possible, he should sleep. Even without drinking it is possible to avoid the torment of thirst. For, though the time is wrong for a drink, the lips and face can be bathed, if they are dry and offensive to the patient himself. It was a nice observation of Erasistratus that the mouth and throat often need liquid when the inner parts do not and that there is no point in making a patient suffer. Such should be the treatment at the beginning.

The best of all medicines is food given at the right time. It remains to determine the time. Many of the ancients fixed it late, on the fifth or even the sixth day. Possibly the climate in Asia or Egypt allows this. Asclepiades, after tiring the patient in every way for three days, proposed to feed him on the fourth. A very recent authority, Themison, took into consideration, not the beginning of the fever, but its cessation or lightening and gave food two days after that – immediately, if there had been no accession of fever; if there had been an accession, he waited till it stopped, or, if persistent, till it lessened. None of these rules is of absolutely universal application. Food may be given on the first day, or on the second, or on the third. It may be withheld till the fourth or fifth. It may be given after one accession, or after two, or after several. The determining factors always are the character of the disease, the state of the body, the climate, the age of the patient, the season of the year. In the great variety of these circumstances there can be no universal rule of time. In a sickness which exhausts the patient's strength food must be given sooner, and so also in a climate in which digestion is quicker. For this reason, it does not seem right for a patient in Africa to fast for a single day. Food should be given sooner to a child than to a young man, in summer than in winter. The one universal rule, good for every time and every place, is this, that the doctor should frequently take a seat beside the sick bed and examine the strength of the patient. So long as the patient has a reserve of strength, let him fight the disease with fasting. As soon as weakness is feared, let him come to the rescue with food. The duty of the doctor is neither to burden the patient with too much food nor weaken him with too little. Erasistratus, I find, knew this. He does not sufficiently make clear how one is to know when the stomach, or when the body itself, is growing weak. But when he says that these points should be observed before food is given, he makes it sufficiently clear that food should not be given while there is a reserve of strength, and that a watch should be kept lest the strength fail. From all this it is clear that one doctor cannot attend upon many patients. The ideal doctor, one who respects his art, is never far from his patient. But those who practise for profit, since there is greater profit in a numerous clientèle, gladly follow a school of teaching which does not demand such constant care. Fevers are a case in point. Even men who rarely see their patients have no difficulty in counting days and accessions. The man who is to see the only thing that really matters, namely when the patient is becoming too weak, must be constant at the bedside.

I have no space for further description of this book. Suffice it to say that what has been translated above is but two pages out of four hundred, and though they have been chosen for the special interest of their matter, they are a fair sample of the splendid quality of the whole. Furthermore the work is a balanced whole. Celsus dropped certain aspects of the subject as treated by Aufidius, notably the section or sections on the aetiology of disease. What remains, however, is the best and most comprehensive single work that has come down from antiquity on the maintenance and restoration of health. Aufidius probably flourished in the last half of the first century B.C. The translation was made under Tiberius between A.D. 20 and 40.

In fairness to Celsus it should be mentioned that not all historians accept Marx's view that the work *On Medicine* is an adaptation of a single source. The older opinion, expressed, for example, by Wellman in *Pauly-Wissowa* in 1901, was that the treatise was a compilation from several sources; and Sir Clifford Allbutt, in his *Greek Medicine in Rome* (1921), is still of this opinion and would interpret the word 'compilation' in a way that would allow a large share of originality, as a writer, though not, of course, as a practitioner, to Celsus. In any case it must be remembered that *On Medicine* is only the fourth part of an encyclopaedic work constructed according to a grand plan designed to cover the whole of life. The four parts were agriculture, medicine, rhetoric, and the art of war. The first two were concerned with the physical life of man, the second two with his life as a citizen. The art of agriculture provides the means of life, that of medicine the means of a healthy life. Medicine protects what agriculture creates. Similarly rhetoric, in the comprehensive sense it then bore, provided a complete training for the citizen in the arts of civil life, so that it might be said to create the civil life which the military art protects. To the work as a whole, then, we cannot deny the credit of being a new construction out of a variety of Greek materials exhibiting the characteristic Roman virtues of organization and design. In comparison with the design of Varro's earlier encyclopaedia we may detect perhaps a greater emphasis on the practical. Varro's extraordinary erudition produced a rounded circle of nine subjects the acquisition of which would certainly have produced an individual of rare academic attainments. Celsus seems to have cared less for culture and sought to provide his generation with a conspectus of the basic arts on which the life of the individual and society depend. Varro's is like a programme for the Arts Faculty of a University. Celsus has provided manuals for four professional schools.

PLINY

When we pass from Varro and Celsus to the third great Roman encyclopaedist, Pliny, it is not so easy to define the character of his work. It has been most variously estimated in modern times. The great French naturalist Buffon (1707–1788) overestimates his merits, but rightly judges the character of the *work* when he says that it deals with all the natural sciences and all the human arts, and the character of the *writer*, when he says that 'he has that facility for taking large views which multiplies science' and that 'he communicates to his readers a certain freedom of spirit, a boldness of thought which is the seed of philosophy'. A work which deals with all the sciences and all the arts and is the work of one man, is bound to be uneven in quality and dismaying to the reader by reason of its multifariousness. The younger Pliny, praising his uncle's book, said that it was 'not less various than Nature herself'. Nevertheless, although it is difficult to see the wood for the trees, there is order as well as grandeur in the plan.

By far the best book on Pliny is that by Littré, disciple of Comte, editor of Hippocrates, and famous lexicographer. He thus defines the plan of *The Natural History*. 'The author begins by setting forth ideas on the universe, the earth, the sun, the planets and the remarkable properties of the elements. From this he passes to the geographical description of the parts of the earth known to the ancients. After the geography comes what we should call natural history, to wit, the history of terrestrial animals, fish, insects and birds. The botanical section which follows is extensive, the more so because Pliny introduces much information on the arts, such as the manufacture of wine and oil, the cultivation of cereals, and various industrial applications. The botanical section concluded, he returns to the animals in order to enumerate the remedies which they supply. Finally he passes to mineral substances and, in what is one of the most interesting parts of his book, he gives at once an account of the methods of extraction of these substances and of the painting and sculpture of the ancients.'

So much for the plan and the general nature of the contents. What of the work in detail? Pliny was a self-taught man who extracted the material for his encyclopaedia out of some two thousand books by some five hundred authors, mostly Greek. Admitting the likelihood that many of the Greek authorities he cites are quoted at second-hand from previous Latin compilations, it was still a work of enormous erudition and labour. With what degree of success was it performed? Nobody is now ever likely to contest the judgment of the judicious and sympathetic Littré, that 'scientific understanding, in the proper sense of the term, is nowhere to be found in him'. Yet the book remains of extraordinary value. Lynn Thorndike remarks of it in his *History of Magic and Experimental Science* that it 'is perhaps the most important single source extant for the history of ancient civilization'. This results not only from its comprehensiveness and variety but from its point of view.

This point of view, already indicated correctly by Buffon, is more fully defined by de Blainville (*Histoire des Sciences de l'organization,* I, p. 336), on the whole an unfavourable critic of Pliny, in this happy description of the book : 'It is a stock-taking, an inventory, an historical catalogue of what man had done up to that time with natural bodies.' It cannot be said (as Francis Bacon charged) that this point of view is totally absent from the natural histories of the Greeks. Theophrastus, for instance, has many indications of the industrial uses of timber and of stones. But nowhere else does this constitute the informing spirit of an ancient natural history. Man for Pliny is in the centre of the picture and determines his choice of material. It is to this fact we owe it that, if he talks of metals, it leads to coinage, to finger-rings (including a disquisition on the middle-class, the Equites, at Rome), to seals and the administration of Italy by Maecenas in the absence of Octavius. It is to this fact we owe that, if he talks of animals, he passes on to describe the medical remedies derived from them. And so on throughout his book.

Another French writer (Egger: *Examen critique des historiens anciens de la vie et règne d'Auguste*, Sect. vii, p. 183) has well illustrated the novelty of the information we sometimes find in Pliny owing to the point of view from which he writes. 'Would Tacitus ever have told us that on the German frontier the captains of auxiliary bands in the service of the Romans used their native troops to hunt a kind of wild goose, the feathers of which were used to stuff pillows for the use of the Roman soldiers? Would Tacitus ever have condescended to tell us that the skins of hedgehogs were the object of an immense commercial activity in the Roman empire, that disorders resulting from monopoly in this commerce were at all times a cause of anxious concern to government and that more senatorial decrees exist on this subject than on any other!' But these details, unusual as they are, are not the most important of his contributions to social history. The opening of his eighteenth book is occupied with a brief but masterly sketch of the history of landed property in Italy and the provinces. Egger rightly remarks that, if Pliny is often mistaken in the history of the arts, the old savant, who had been consul, general and admiral, is an authority of the first order on a sociological question of this kind. The more remarkable then is his famous verdict: 'If we admit the truth, it was the system of large estates which ruined Italy and is now also ruining the provinces.'

The frankness of mind and incisiveness of style revealed in this passage mark many a page of this strange encyclopaedia. Indeed in a very true sense Pliny's *Natural History* should be regarded as the prototype of Voltaire's *Dictionnaire Philosophique*. It gives him a chance to air his opinions on everything. Hence that freedom and elevation of which Buffon spoke. There is even humour, in the English sense. Thus, after a pregnant and epigrammatic dissertation on the varieties of religious belief, he concludes in this vein : 'For the imperfections of nature as revealed in man a peculiar consolation is this, that not even God can do everything. He could not, for instance, if he wanted to, commit suicide, which, in the trials of our mortal life, is his best gift to men. He cannot make mortals immortal, recall the dead, bring it about that one who has lived has not lived, or that one who has borne office has not borne office. He has no power over the past but oblivion, and, if I may be excused for illustrating our fellowship with God by trivial examples, he cannot make it that twice ten should not be twenty, and so on. By all this is unmistakably revealed the power of nature and the fact that it is this power we call God. I hope I may be pardoned this digression into what I fear have become commonplaces owing to the never-ending debate about God.' (Bk. II, 27.)

And here, in conclusion, is another passage, which owes some of its arguments to Lucretius, but is completely personal and characteristic. 'Beyond the grave lie the empty speculations about the spirits of the dead. For every man it will be the same after his last day as it was before his first. After death neither body nor spirit will have sensation any more than they did before he was born. This vanity of staking a claim on the future and imagining for oneself a life in the season of death takes various forms : the immortality of the soul, the transmigration of souls, the life of the shades in the underworld, the worship of the spirits of the dead, even the deification of one who has already ceased to be a man. As if, forsooth, we drew our breath in any way that could distinguish us from the other animals ; as if there were not many creatures who live longer than we do, for whom nobody has imagined a similar immortality. These are the inventions of a childish folly, of a mortality greedy of never ceasing to be. Plague take it, what madness is this of repeating life in death? How shall those born ever rest, if sense is to remain with the soul on high or with the ghost below? Nay, this fond fancy destroys nature's chief blessing, death, and doubles the smart of him that is to die by the calculation of what is still to come. If life is to be so sweet, who can find it sweet to have ceased to live? But how much happier, how much more sure, that every man should come to trust himself and take from his proven insensibility of what was before he was born his warrant of the peace that is to be.' The author of these words lived an active, cheerful life in the service of his fellow-men and died an adventurous death while making too close an observation of Vesuvius in eruption.

GEMINUS

We pass now to the consideration of scientific works of this period written in Greek and come at once to a masterpiece of exposition in the *Introduction to Astronomy* of Geminus. This man (whose name is probably to be pronounced with the middle syllable long, and not like the Latin for twin) seems to have been a native of Rhodes and to have flourished about 70 B.C. He was a pupil of the great Stoic philosopher Posidonius and wrote a voluminous commentary to a work of his on astronomy. Later he himself made an epitome of his own commentary. This work remained in use for centuries but has not reached us in the form in which Geminus left it. In the fourth or fifth century, probably in Constantinople, portions of it were excerpted and trimmed with a little additional material. So came into being the astronomical manual we now possess under the title of *Geminus's Introduction to Astronomy*. It is a valuable source for our knowledge of Greek positional astronomy, mathematical geography, and calendar-making. Manitius, its most recent editor (Teubner, 1898), detects errors as well as omissions in it, which, however, he lays mainly at the door of the Constantinopolitan excerpter. Wellman finds it free from prejudices and superstition and based throughout on scientific research. The French scholar, Paul Tannéry, is enthusiastic, regarding it as one of the best extant works of antiquity. Heath is lukewarm, describing it as 'a tolerable elementary treatise suitable for teaching purposes and containing the most important doctrines of Greek astronomy represented from the standpoint of Hipparchus'. Being myself one who needs a Hipparchus-made-easy, and finding it in this book, I persist in calling it, as a text-book, a masterpiece.

Readers of our first volume will already have met (p. 86) an excellent example of the simple expository style of Geminus, namely, the passage in which he explains that astronomers have always constructed their science on the supposition insisted upon by the Pythagorean philosophers : that the motion of the heavenly bodies must be assumed to be circular and uniform. It is important to notice that Geminus has no quarrel with this. In a fragment of his original *Epitome*, which survives independently of the text-book made in Constantinople, he deals with this point. He approves of a significant division of labour between the philosopher and the astronomer, according to which it is for the philosopher to lay down principles within the limits of which the astronomer must work out coherent explanations of the celestial phenomena. But the clarity with which he expounds this division of labour is all of a piece with the clarity which reigns everywhere in his book. We can best exhibit the quality of the exposition within the limits at our disposal by first giving the chapter headings of the whole and then quoting at length the context of the now familiar passage about the Pythagoreans.

The eighteen chapters in the edition of Manitius have the following titles: *The circle of the zodiac. The order and position of the twelve signs. The shapes of the signs. The axis and the poles. The celestial circles. Day and night. The times of rising of the twelve signs. The months. The phases of the moon. The eclipse of the sun. The eclipse of the moon. That the planets have a motion opposite to that of the cosmos. Risings and settings. The circles of the fixed stars. The terrestrial zones. The habitable portions of the globe. The use of the stars as weather signs. Synodic and other months.* To this is appended a calendar, or table of the time taken by the sun to traverse each of the twelve signs, and the accompanying weather signs.

Now for our quotation:

The times between the tropics and the equinoxes are divided in the following way. From the spring equinox to the summer tropic 94½ days. That is the number of days in which the sun passes through the Ram, the Bull, and the Twins and arriving in the first degree of the Crab makes the summer tropic. From the summer tropic to the autumn equinox 92½ days. That is the number of days in which the sun passes through the Crab, the Lion and the Maid and arriving in the first degree of the Scales makes the autumn equinox. From the autumn equinox to the winter tropic 88⅛ days. That is the number of days in which the sun passes through the Scales, the Scorpion, and the Archer and arriving in the first degree of Capricorn makes the winter tropic. From the winter tropic to the spring equinox 90⅛ days. For that is the number of days in which the sun passes through the remaining three signs of the zodiac, Capricorn, Aquarius, and the Fishes. The total of all the days in these four periods is 365, and that is the number of days we found in the year.

Here the question arises, how it is that, the four quarters of the zodiacal circle being equal and the sun moving always at a uniform speed, he yet traverses unequal arcs in equal times. For there underlies the whole science of astronomy the assumption that the sun and the moon and the five planets move at even speeds in perfect circles in an opposite direction to the cosmos. It was the Pythagoreans, the first to approach these questions, who laid down the hypothesis of a circular and uniform motion for the sun, moon, and planets. Their view was that, in regard of divine and eternal beings, a supposition of such disorder as that these bodies should move now more quickly and now more slowly, or should even stop, as in what are called the stations of the planets, is inadmissible. Even in the human sphere such irregularity is incompatible with the orderly procedure of a gentleman. And even if the crude necessities of life often impose upon men occasions of haste or loitering, it is not to be supposed that such occasions inhere in the incorruptible nature of the stars. For this reason they defined their problem as the explanation of the phenomena on the hypothesis of circular and uniform motion.

About the other stars we shall give the explanation in another place. Here we shall explain how it is that the sun, though moving at a uniform speed, traverses equal arcs in unequal times.

What is called the sphere of the fixed stars, which contains all the imagery of the signs of the zodiac, is the highest of all. It must not be supposed that all the stars lie on a single surface, but that some are higher and some lower. However, to the limitations of our vision the difference in height is not apparent. Below the sphere of the fixed stars lies Saturn, which traverses the zodiac in about 30 years, one sign in 2 years and 6 months. Below Saturn is Jupiter, which traverses the zodiac in 12 years, a sign a year. Next lowest is Mars, which traverses the zodiac in $2\frac{1}{2}$ years, a sign every $2\frac{1}{2}$ months. The sun holds the next place, traversing the circle of the zodiac in a year, and each sign in about a month. Below it is Venus, which moves at about the same speed as the sun. Next comes Mercury, which also moves at the same speed as the sun. Lowest of all is the moon, which traverses the zodiac in $27\frac{1}{3}$ days, and a sign in about $2\frac{1}{4}$ days.

Now if the sun moved at the same distance as the stars which form the signs of the zodiac, then certainly we would have found the times between the tropics and equinoxes equal to one another. Moving at uniform speed the sun must cover equal arcs in equal times. Similarly, supposing that the sun is lower than the circle of the zodiac but moves about the same centre as the circle of the zodiac, then also the times between tropics and equinoxes would have been equal. All circles described about the same centre are similarly divided by their diameters. Since the circle of the zodiac is divided into four equal parts by the diameters which lie between the tropic and equinoctial points, necessarily the circle of the sun would be divided into four equal parts by the same diameters. Moving thus at uniform speed in his own sphere the sun would have made the times of the four quarters equal. But in fact the sun moves not only on a lower but on an eccentric circle, as the accompanying figure shows (see p. 142). The centre of the circle is not the same as that of the zodiacal circle, but is thrust to one side. On account of this position the course of the sun is divided into four unequal parts. The greatest part of its circumference lies beneath the quarter of the zodiacal circle extending from the first degree of the Ram to the 30th degree of the Twins. The smallest part of its circumference lies beneath the quarter of the zodiacal circle extending from the first degree of the Scales to the 30th degree of the Archer.

Naturally therefore the sun moving uniformly in its own circle traverses unequal arcs in unequal times, the longest arc in the longest time, the shortest in the shortest. When it traverses the longest arc on its own circle, then it passes the quarter of the zodiac from the spring equinox to the summer tropic. When it moves over the shortest arc on its own circle, then it passes the quarter of the zodiac from the autumn equinox to the winter tropic. Since unequal arcs of the sun's circle lie beneath equal arcs of the zodiacal circle, inevitably the times between the tropics and the equinoxes are unequal, and the greatest time is that from the spring equinox to the summer tropic, the shortest from the autumn equinox to the winter tropic. The sun therefore moves always at uniform speed, but owing to the eccentricity of its circle it traverses the four quarters of the zodiac in unequal times.

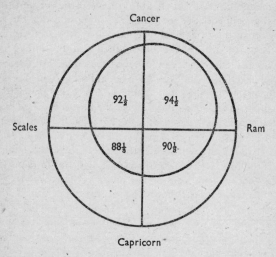

This long passage has been translated literally. Its style is repetitive and full, which makes the reading a little tedious. But we were anxious at all costs to preserve the text-book quality of the original, in which the writer leaves nothing to chance.

STRABO

Geminus's *Elements of Astronomy* is a compact manual, a schoolbook, at least in the form in which we now have it. The next book to which we shall turn, the *Geography* of Strabo, is a large-scale work which for once has survived all but entire in its original form. Strabo was a native of

Amasia in Pontus. He was born in 64 or 63 B.C., and his
geography is thought to have been composed in the last
decade of the pagan era. Its purpose was no less than to give
a reliable and readable account of all the different countries
of the habitable world which should be fully abreast of contemporary geographical science in all its branches. Readable
and reliable it is, but it had to wait to be read. That Strabo
aimed at a wide public is certain. He had lived at Alexandria, he had frequently visited Rome, and he is careful to
insist on the importance of geography for the administrator.
But it is probable that his book was written immediately for
Pythodoris, Queen of Pontus, and published there. If so,
Pontus did not prove a good publishing centre. His book
remained unknown at Rome. Even the omnivorous Pliny
had not heard of it. The Romans satisfied their geographical
thirst with the relevant chapters of Pliny himself, which are
not among his best, and the brief and superficial com-
pendium of Pomponius Mela (c. 45 A.D.). It was not till after
the foundation of Constantinople that Strabo came into his
own. For the Byzantine world he was an authority. From
Byzantium his book came to Western Europe at the Renaissance. It has sometimes been disparaged, but never forgotten
since. Its centuries of neglect, which could be paralleled in
the history of many other great books, remind us that when
we know the contents of such books we are still far from
knowing the history of the effective spread of science in the
world. Strabo represents the level of achievement of his
science in the Augustan Age, but probably very few Augus-
tans had read him.

The unification of the world under Roman rule gave
opportunities for the development of geographical knowledge and Strabo has a refreshing sense of the need to bring
his subject up to date. His early chapters are filled with criticism of his predecessors, summoned for cross-examination

in order, as he says, to justify his attempt by showing how greatly the subject stood in need of correction and addition (Bk. II, 4, 8). A glance at the history of geography will clarify his position.

Geography was an ancient science, but it owed little to any people other than the Greeks. It might have been expected that the Phoenicians, who preceded the Greeks as explorers and masters of the Mediterranean, would have laid the foundation of the science. In a limited sense, they did. Strabo recalls, for instance, that the Bear was not recognized as a constellation until the Phoenicians began to steer by it, and that it was from them an understanding of its use reached the Greeks. But in general the Phoenicians kept their knowledge to themselves, filling the world not with science but with fabulous stories of the difficulties attendant on the approach to the distant sources of their precious articles of commerce. Their contribution to science was as unintentional as that of monopolistic trusts at the present day. It was left for the Ionian Greeks to take the first steps. They, as we have seen (Vol. I, p. 29), were great colonizers. Strabo tells us that many Ionian and other colonizing expeditions had in early days come to grief for lack of geographical knowledge. The map of Anaximander, and the pioneer geographical treatise of Hecataeus, also of Miletus, written about 520 B.C., were the response to this situation. But, as was characteristic of these Ionian Greeks, out of the knowledge won to meet a practical need sprang a science which has remained to enrich the world.

The complex science of geography has been conveniently divided into four subdivisions: mathematical, physical, descriptive and political, and historical. All these branches were implicit in the work of the earliest Greek pioneers. Anaximander, who introduced the use of the gnomon to Greece, as well as made the first map, may be given the credit for founding mathematical geography. Physical geography found exponents in the poet-philosopher Xenophanes, who detected the phenomenon of raised beaches in the presence of shells and marine fossils inland, and in Herodotus, who accepts the opinion that the whole of the Nile Delta has been formed by alluvial deposits and speculates on how many thousand years it would take it to fill the Arabian Gulf if the Nile reversed its course. The beginnings of political and of historical geography are to be found in Herodotus, in Thucydides, in the Hippocratic tract *Airs Waters Places*, where descriptions of peoples and their institutions begin to be related to their habitat. Nor did this impulse to grasp the nature of the habitable world soon expire. Xenophon in his *March of the Ten Thousand* (401 B.C.) opened up the geography of Armenia. That doughty mariner, Pytheas of Marseilles (about 310 B.C.), a pioneer of scientific and commercial exploration, did the same for Britain and neighbouring seas and lands.

A second great period in the history of Greek geography came with the foundation of Alexandria and the conquests of Alexander in the East. At Alexandria geography could not fail to share in the mathematical advances of the time. With Eratosthenes the determination of latitudes by the sun-dial became the rule, although the number of determinations remained small. He estimated the dimensions of the globe and the shape and extent of the habitable portion of it, and, in carrying out his ambition to reform the map of the world, he drew across the parallelogram which represented the *oikoumene* (or inhabited world) eight parallels of latitude and seven meridians of longitude. The meridians were fixed by dead reckoning. Though later Hipparchus suggested the use of observations of lunar eclipses for determinations of longitude, this remained no more than a suggestion. Astronomical determinations of longitude were not effected in antiquity. The organization of science remained below its theory.

Turning to the other branches of the science, we find that both physical and political geography were strikingly advanced by Posidonius, the Stoic philosopher of Rhodes, already referred to as the teacher of Geminus. He is criticized by Strabo for 'being too interested in causes in the manner of Aristotle'. Like Aristotle, however, he was very willing to use his eyes. His accounts of Spain and Gaul, both the countries and their inhabitants, were filled with observation and thought. Tozer has called him 'the most intelligent traveller in antiquity'. Other great exponents of political geography were Megasthenes and Agatharcides. The former (c. 290 B.C.) was the agent of the Seleucids at Palibothra on the Ganges. His account of Northern India, surviving in the borrowings of later writers, was remarkable for its fulness and accuracy. The latter, Agatharcides (c. 170–100 B.C.), penned an account of the Ethiopian gold mines and gold miners, which, preserved for us in the pages of Diodorus, is perhaps the most famous piece of descriptive sociology of antiquity. With the historians Ephorus and Polybius historical geography became a systematic study. Such had been the achievements of geography in its various branches when Strabo set out to renew the subject under the favourable conditions of the Augustan age.

It will be readily understood that no one man is likely to be equally competent in all branches of such a large and complex science. Where Strabo was weak was in mathematics. Here he was perhaps hardly abreast of the Alexandrians of the age of Eratosthenes. Everywhere else he contributed something of importance. In physical geography he has had the good fortune to earn the praise of Lyell for two anticipations of modern science. (1) He stresses the importance of inferring great past terrestrial changes from the smaller changes which take place before our eyes. (2) In discussing certain somewhat superficial views of Strato on the flow from the Euxine into the Aegean, and the supposed flow from the Mediterranean into the Atlantic, he shows an arresting boldness of thought in advancing the hypothesis of alternate elevations and depressions of ocean beds. But his real greatness is in descriptive and historical geography. Only extensive reading in his seventeen books can give a true impression of his powers as a descriptive or political geographer. Within the limits of our space it will be best to concentrate on his remarkable grasp of principle in the remaining field, that of historical geography.

Geographical determinism is a common error, not confined to modern science. The ancients too had sinned in this respect. Strabo is free of the fault. In many passages he shows an understanding, remarkable for his age, of the truth that the influence of geography and climate on a people is a very complex and difficult enquiry, not to be interpreted as a direct effect of nature on man, but as varying according to the level of industrial and political technique. 'The various arts, professions, and institutions of mankind,' he writes, 'once they have been introduced, flourish in almost any latitude and even in spite of the latitude. If some local characteristics come by nature, others come by habit and practice. It is not by nature that the Athenians are fond of letters, while the Spartans, and even the Thebans who live still nearer to them, are not. It is rather by habit. Similarly training and habit account for the various proficiencies of the Babylonian and Egyptian peoples' (Bk. II, 3, 7). His grasp of this principle makes Strabo a scientific observer of the advance of Classical civilization among backward peoples.

The favourable prospects for the advance of this civilization in Europe are analysed in a famous description of the continent, of which we quote a part. 'Of the habitable part of Europe the cold mountainous regions furnish by nature only a wretched existence to their inhabitants, yet even the haunts of poverty and piracy become civilized when they get good administrators. The Greeks are an example. They lived among rocky mountains, but lived well, because they took thought for the art of politics, for the arts of production, and for the art of living. The Romans again have taken over many people that were by nature savage because the places they inhabited were rocky, harbourless, cold or in some other way unsuited to a numerous population, and by bringing the isolated communities into touch with one another have brought them from savagery to civilization. Where Europe is level and temperate, nature co-operates to these ends. In a country blessed by nature everything tends towards peace, as in a country cursed by nature men are brave and warlike. Each kind of country can receive benefits from the other, the latter helping with arms, the former with agricultural and industrial produce and the training of character. But if they fail to help one another, the mutual harm they inflict is obvious. The violence of the warriors might indeed carry the day, if not counterbalanced by the greater numbers of the peaceable. But against this danger Europe is armed by nature. Throughout its whole extent it is diversified by plains and mountains so that everywhere the agricultural and civilized population dwells side by side with the warlike, but the peace-loving population is the more numerous and maintains control over the whole. The Greeks, the Macedonians and the Romans have presided successively over the accomplishment of this civilizing process. For the reasons given Europe is markedly self-sufficient both for peace and war. The warlike population is abundant, and so is that which tills her soil and maintains her cities. She has the further advantage that she produces the best and most necessary fruits and all the useful metals, importing from abroad such inessential luxuries as spices and precious stones. Furthermore flocks and herds are numerous and wild

animals rare. Such is a general description of this continent.'
(Bk. 2, 5, 26).

This is a classical page of geographical science, and there
are many such pages in Strabo. His account, for instance, of
the river system of France – how it opens up the whole
country to internal intercourse of its peoples as well as throw-
ing them open to external influences by connecting the
Ocean with the Inner Sea – has earned the enthusiastic praise
of the brilliant modern geographers of that land (Bk. 4, 1,
4). Almost equally admirable is the account of Italy (Bk. 6,
4, 1). Here the character and situation of the peninsula are
considered from the point of view of its suitability for world
domination, and in his next paragraph he proceeds to 'add
to his account of the country a summary account also of the
Roman people who took possession of it and equipped it as
a base of operations for the universal hegemony', Geopolitics
is hardly a new science.

His brief summary of Roman history has two leading ideas
– that the Roman conquest was reluctant, and that it has
meant the happiness of the conquered through good government. He has here, of course, a splendid theme. 'Replacing
villages and cantons with cities on the shores of the Mediterranean', writes Vidal de la Blache, 'was the master-stroke
of Greece and Rome. Contemporary observers of this phenomenon – Thucydides, Polybius, and Strabo – were not mistaken. They describe the *polis,* or ancient city, as the symbol
and outward evidence of a superior civilization.' Strabo's
justifiable enthusiasm for this process was such that he describes the conquest of his own country of Pontus without
a pang. But the spread of the city civilization at the expense
of the villages and cantons took its terrible toll of human
life and happiness, and of this side of the process Strabo was
an inadequate reporter. It is true he was not blind to the
virtues of the simple tribesmen who were compulsorily

civilized. He has forcible observations on the moral corruption of simple peoples by the spread of civilization, and on
the connection between the growth of property and the
growth of crime (Bk. 7, 3, 4 and 7). But he had at the same
time acquired the convenient habit of discounting the suffer-
ings of the victims of civilization on the score of their presumed insensibility. He offers proof of the brutishness of
simple peoples which are at least as eloquent of the brutality
of their masters. 'When the Roman generals raid the mountain strongholds of these Corsicans and carry them off in
great numbers for slaves, you then have at Rome the opportunity to discover their astonishing brutishness. Either they
are as savage as wild animals or as tame as sheep. Some of
them die in captivity. The rest are so apathetic and slow-
witted that their angry purchasers, though they have bought
them for a song, repent of their bargain' (Bk. 5, 2, 7). Even
more striking is his proof of the brutishness of the rebellious
Cantabrian natives. 'On being crucified after capture they
still kept on shouting their victory slogans from the cross'
(Bk. 3, 4, 18).

But this is by the way, a mere indication of the familiar
fact that the progress of civilization has been a brutal thing.
It is one of the chief lessons of history, but it has no particular bearing on Strabo who merely reflected the temper
of the dominant peoples in his day. Our concern now is with
his place in the history of science, and here his mastery is
incontestable. His seventeen books are the greatest work of
its kind produced in antiquity. We have taken our illustra-
tions from the earlier books. It must not be inferred that the
rest are inferior. Books twelve, thirteen, and fourteen, where
he describes Asia Minor of which he was a native and where
he relies most on personal observation, are among the best.
But he also knew how to select his authorities, and his
account of countries which he had not seen – India, for

example, where he had Megasthenes to guide him – is a storehouse of reliable information. Vast as his design is, his work is not a compilation. The material so industriously collected is firmly controlled and deployed to illustrate great principles, and everywhere we are in the presence not only of a scientist with a point of view but of a writer with a sense of style. He has deserved his great fame and was unfortunate not to win it immediately.

PTOLEMY

The mathematical side of geography in which Strabo was weak found its definitive expression in antiquity at the hands of Ptolemy, who flourished about A.D. 150. Mathematician, astronomer, geographer, physicist, he is one of the outstanding figures in the history of science. As a mathematician and astronomer he carried on and systematized the work of Hipparchus. His greatest mathematical achievement is the exposition of the spherical trigonometry created by Hipparchus. Since trigonometry was invented by Hipparchus for use in astronomy, spherical trigonometry naturally came first. In the first book of the *Almagest,* as we call it after an Arabic corruption of the Greek (Ptolemy himself called it *The Mathematical Collection in Thirteen Books*), after giving the mathematical proofs on which his determinations rested, he constructed a Table of Chords for arcs subtending angles increasing from ½ degree to 180 degrees by steps of ½ degree. This is the equivalent of a Table of sines for angles from ¼ degree to 90 degrees by steps of ¼ degree. It has been observed that this is the most permanent part of his work. For, while the lapse of time has superseded his astronomical system and his map of the world, the basis of trigonometry laid down by Hipparchus and Ptolemy remains unshaken.

The foundation of his system of astronomy is, of course, the geocentric principle of Hipparchus, with a leaning to the method of epicycles rather than eccentrics to explain the varied motions of the heavenly bodies. It is not easy briefly to describe the contents of the thirteen books. Books I and II lay down the mathematical foundation and give general explanations of the motions of the heavenly bodies in relation to the earth as centre. Book III is on the sun and the length of the year. It tells how Hipparchus was led to his discovery of the precession of the equinoxes. It also lays down a principle which has had a long and useful role in science, namely that in explaining phenomena the simplest hypothesis that is not contradicted by the facts is to be preferred. Books IV and V are on the motions of the moon. In his first book Ptolemy had described the instruments he employed for a fundamental measurement, that of the obliquity of the ecliptic. The beginning of the fifth book is taken up with a description of the astrolabe of Hipparchus, which Ptolemy himself also used in confirming the observations of his predecessor. Book VI is on solar and lunar eclipses. VII and VIII are on the fixed stars, and it takes the remaining five to deal with the specially vexed subject of the planets.

It is with this immense astronomical equipment that Ptolemy proceeds to renew the science of mathematical geography. An older contemporary of his, Marinus of Tyre, had again taken up the challenge of Hipparchus, to make a map of the world in which all the principal features should be correctly placed in respect of mathematically determined parallels of latitude and meridians of longitude. It is as the corrector and completer of Marinus that Ptolemy puts himself forward. The arrangement of his book was original and convenient for reference, and this increased its authority. Of its eight books the first and the last are concerned with mathematical and astronomical principles and discussions,

but the central six books are made up of tables, giving the
names of the places which figured on the maps of the different countries at that time, together with their latitudes and
longitudes. The boundaries of the various countries are also
defined and there are explanatory remarks of various kinds.
But the essential of the treatise is the catalogue of names of
places together with the authoritative-looking determinations
of position.

This appearance of authority is, in fact, delusive. Some
half-dozen latitudes only had been astronomically determined
– Marseilles, Rome, Rhodes, Alexandria, Syene, perhaps a
few more. No longitudes were astronomically determined.
Within a frame of insecurely fixed parallels and meridians
positions were obtained by reducing roughly measured distances to degrees. Some distances on land had been paced.
Others were estimated in still rougher ways. At sea – for the
use of the log was unknown – distances were guessed by
times. By a singular misfortune the method of reducing distances to degrees was vitiated by a false figure. Hipparchus
had arrived at a very correct determination of the circumference of the globe. Posidonius had 'corrected' this, reducing it to five-sixths of the first figure. Accordingly only 500
stadia (50 geographical miles) went to the degree instead of
600 stadia (60 geographical miles). Ptolemy adopted the
erroneous figure of Posidonius. This meant that all his distances, invariably exaggerated in any case by the travellers
who made them, were exaggerated a further 20 per cent
in the hands of the expert. From the time of Dicaearchus
(c. 310 B.C.) the most important line on the globe for Greek
geographers had been the parallel of 36 degrees of latitude
which runs through the Straits of Gibraltar at one end of the
Mediterranean and the Island of Rhodes at the other. But
what lay on or near this parallel? Ptolemy made it pass
through Caralis in Sardinia and Lilybaeum in Sicily, errors

respectively of over 3 and just under 2 degrees. Worse still, he put Carthage, which really lies nearly a degree north of it, more than a degree south of it. This wonderfully evened out the coastline of North Africa. His prime meridian was also unfortunate. He followed Marinus in placing this in the Canaries, but he supposed these islands to lie about 7 degrees east of their true position. All his calculations of distance were in fact based on Alexandria, but since for the purposes of his map-making they had all to be referred to his prime meridian he imported an error of 7 degrees into every position. Such were the general errors pervading his calculations. There were also particular ones due to various contingencies. He accidentally rotated his map of Scotland through an angle of 90 degrees so that it juts out to the east of England instead of extending north. In the Far East he was out of his range and makes Ceylon fourteen times its real size!

These errors are, of course, important. Nevertheless there is nothing easier than to exaggerate their significance. To convince oneself of this it is only necessary to look at the map of the world as known to Homer, with the River Ocean encircling the flat disk of the world, and set beside it the map which can be reconstructed from the data of Ptolemy, with its curved parallels and curved meridians, its fulness and comparative accuracy in regions about the Inner Sea, and its immense reach from Ireland in the North-west corner to vague indications of China and Malaya in the East. Still more convincing is it of the genuine worth of his science to look at the 'wheel maps' of the Middle Ages, in which the River Ocean again encircles a flat disk with Jerusalem at the centre and Paradise at the top, maps out of which all the laboriously acquired mathematics and astronomy of the Greek scientists have been drained. In such a setting we judge the achievement of Ptolemy and the other Greek geographers aright.

It only remains to add a word on another aspect of his work. He was not only a great observer, as his description of astronomical instruments and the use he made of them, prove. He was also an experimentalist. The fifth book of his treatise on *Optics* contains observations on the refraction of light. This was bound to be of interest to astronomers who had knowledge, among other such refractive phenomena, of an eclipsed moon rising over against a setting sun. Ptolemy gives tables of refraction for various angles of incidence in experiments with air, water, and glass, and tries to work out a law. We observe here, as elsewhere, a combination of insight and system characteristic of the man.

GALEN

Passing from the great world of nature to the little world of man, we find in Galen (A.D. 129–199) one who holds the same place in the history of medicine as Ptolemy does in the history of astronomy and geography. As the astronomy and geography of the Renaissance resume and correct the work of Ptolemy, so do its anatomy and physiology resume and correct the work of Galen. We must attempt briefly to characterize his work, but it is a task of exceptional difficulty. Of his voluminous writings on a wide variety of subjects about a hundred genuine works under separate titles are extant. Kühn's edition (1821–1833), the only complete modern one, fills, together with the translation in Latin, twenty large volumes. Among this mass of material the experts with difficulty find their way, and the layman is confused by contradictory verdicts. But it is perhaps fair to say that the practising physicians who have written of him in modern times rank him higher than the academic critics. At all events we must recognize that this extraordinarily fluent writer, who from an early age poured out controversial books, not only on the various medical sects, but on the various philosophical schools, and in a general way on cultural and educational subjects, was also a most diligent observer and researcher. His therapeutical, physiological and anatomical works were based on a first-hand acquaintance with nature which would have done credit to one who had not also found time to interest himself in so many other questions.

Some assistance in finding one's way through Galen's works is provided by a little tract on his own writings which special circumstances induced him to write. From this we draw the following interesting particulars. Once upon a time, in Shoemakers' Street in Rome, where most of the book-shops were, Galen witnessed a scene that must have delighted his author's heart. A book was displayed bearing the name Doctor Galen. A discussion began as to whether it was a genuine work of Galen's. An educated man, attracted by the title, bought it and began to read it at once to find out what it was about. He had not read two lines before he flung it aside exclaiming : 'The style isn't Galen's. The title is false.' He, Galen comments approvingly, had had a good old-fashioned Greek education at the hands of the grammarians and rhetoricians. But times have changed. Aspirants to medicine and philosophy, without having learned to read properly, attend lectures on these subjects vainly hoping to understand teachings which are the noblest known to men. Accordingly to avoid false ascriptions to him of inferior writings Galen proposes to list and describe his genuine works. He has the additional ground for fear that he knows that manifold defacements of his works are occurring on every hand. In different countries different teachers are reading out, as their own, works of Galen that have suffered additions, subtractions and alterations. Friends have advised him of the necessity of his coming to the rescue of his own reputation, and he has had proof of the soundness of their advice.

The third chapter of the little tract *On His Own Books*, from which we have derived the above particulars, describes his anatomical researches and writings. A portion of this we shall translate in full, for his anatomical works are his most important contribution to science. 'First comes a book *On the Bones* for beginners. After this come other books for beginners, one concerning dissection of the veins and arteries, another that of the nerves. There is also one briefly recapitulating all the instruction on the muscles which is to be found in my *Anatomical Exercises*. If anybody, after reading the primer *On the Bones*, wants to pass straight to the *Anatomical Exercises,* he can skip the primers on the veins and arteries and on the muscles. He will find everything in the *Exercises*. In them the first book is about the muscles and sinews of the hand, the second about the muscles and sinews of the legs, the third about the nerves and vessels in the limbs. The fourth is about the muscles that move the jaws and the lips, the chin, the head, the neck and the shoulders. The fifth is about the muscles controlling the chest, belly, loins and back. The sixth is about the nutritive organs, namely the stomach, gut, liver, spleen, kidneys, bladder and the rest. The seventh and eighth contain the anatomy of the parts concerned with breathing. The seventh describes the dissection and the vivisection of heart, lung and arteries. The eighth deals with the contents of the whole thorax. The ninth gives the dissection of the brain and the spine. The tenth that of the eyes, tongue, throat and neighbouring parts. The eleventh that of the larynx and of what is called the hyoid bone, of the parts connected thereto and the incoming nerves. The twelfth deals with the arteries and the veins. The thirteenth with the nerves springing from the brain. The fourteenth with those from the spine. The fifteenth with the organs of generation.

These are the essentials of anatomy, but there is much besides that is useful. For this I have provided by reducing the twenty books of Marinus *On Anatomy* to four, and all the works of Lycus to two. A table of contents of these works follows.'

The extraordinary importance of this anatomical research is obvious. True, the dissections were performed on monkeys, not on men; but this was a source of error unavoidable in the circumstances of the time. It was the resumption of this programme of dissection at the Renaissance, particularly by Vesalius, that laid the foundation of modern anatomy. Harvey, whose discovery of the circulation of the blood was destined to destroy the Galenic physiology, had been trained in the Galenic programme of dissections in the Vesalian school of Padua.

A word must now be said about the physiology of Galen. Like the astronomy of the time it rested partly on observation and partly on a body of philosophical principles which at the time seemed certainly true but which modern physiology has had to modify or discard. The various types of living things had long been classed in three great divisions – plants, animals, and men. Plants embodied the principle of growth, animals the principles of growth and locomotion, men the principles of growth, locomotion, and reason. It was the opinion of the Stoics, an opinion derived from various sources, that *pneuma* (or air), drawn in from the cosmos whose breath it was, was the vital principle of these three grades of living things. The physiological function of the complex human organism was to adapt this external pneuma to the three grades of life manifested in man, growth, locomotion, and thought. In its first adaptation the pneuma became *natural spirit* and caused growth. In its second adaptation it became *vital spirit* and caused locomotion. In its third adaptation it became *animal spirit* (from *anima*, the

soul) and caused thought. Galen with elaborate ingenuity
fitted what he knew of the digestive, respiratory, and nervous
systems of man to the explanation of this threefold function
of the human organism. The liver and the veins were the
principal organs of the vegetable life of man. The heart, with
the lungs and arteries, maintained the animal life. The brain
and the nervous system were the seat of the intellectual life,
the distinctive part of man, the rational animal.

We may briefly describe the functioning of his system. In
the liver the ingested food was converted into blood which
was distributed by the veins for the growth of the body.
The motion of the blood in the veins was conceived of as a
sort of sluggish oscillation to and from the liver. From the
liver it came by the portal vein to the right ventricle of the
heart. Here it parted with its impurities, which were carried
off by the pulmonary artery to the lung and thence exhaled.
A portion of this purified blood was reserved for the second
adaptation. It passed through the septum into the left ventricle, where it met again with pneuma from the outer world
conveyed from the lung to the left ventricle by the pulmonary
vein, and there, in the left ventricle, it was elaborated into
vital spirit and distributed through the body by the arteries.
Of the arteries some lead to the brain. The arterial blood
which is sent to the brain passed through a network of vessels
known as the *rete mirabile*. Here took place the third adaptation. This portion of the blood became endowed with animal spirit and was distributed throughout the body by the
nerves. The system is complete and neat. It took account of
an enormous number of observed facts and interpreted them
in the light of a philosophy which the wisdom of generations
seemed to have confirmed. Galen must have found it impossible to imagine that it could be false. We, who know
that it is false, may profitably ask how it could ever come to
be shaken.

The explanation, of course, is that essential parts of the theory rest on faulty observation. The account of the transformation of venous into arterial blood cannot be correct, for it assumes that blood passes through the septum which is, in fact, a solid wall of muscle. Equally incorrect is the account of the transformation of the arterial blood into blood endowed with animal spirits. The organ (the *rete mirabile*) in which it is supposed to take place, though prominent in ruminants, where Galen had seen it, does not exist in man. With the revival of anatomical research in modern times these fatal obstacles to the Galenic physiology became clear. For long, however, they merely constituted knotty problems but did not destroy the theory. The Galenic physiology had features which blinded enquirers to the essential truth awaiting discovery. It was difficult to get a correct idea of the circulation of the blood when one had learned from Galen that there were three different kinds of blood each with its own mode of distribution. Nor, even for those who knew that the septum is solid, was the heart's action easy to understand. For Galen the real work of the heart was done in the *diastole*, or expansion, which was supposed to suck air from the lungs. How was one to be sure that the real work was done in the *systole*, or contraction, which propels the blood through the arteries? Harvey sat many hours a day for many years looking at beating hearts, or holding a beating heart in one hand and a pulsing artery in the other, instructing his brain through his fingers, feeling his way to the truth, before he succeeded in reversing Galen's view, first in his own mind, then slowly in the world at large. Even then it was Galen who had triumphed over Galen, Galen the observer who had triumphed over Galen the philosopher, for it was Galen's technique Harvey had learned at Padua.

It remains to add a few particulars about Galen's life. Like nearly all the great scientists of Greek and Roman times he came from the east. He was born in Pergamum, where his father was an architect and mathematician. He studied medicine first at Pergamum, then at Smyrna, Corinth, and Alexandria. On completing his training he was surgeon to the gladiators in his native town for four years. I wish we had a precise account of his duties in this post, a picture of his working day. Subsequently he was attracted to Rome, where provincials then went to seek their fortunes. We know that he there enjoyed immense repute and that his services were required by the Emperor, Marcus Aurelius, who wanted him as his physician on an expedition against the German tribes. Somewhere in the intervals of a busy life he found the time to prescribe, dissect and write.

BIBLIOGRAPHICAL NOTE

For the Latin grammarians see Keil, *Grammatici Latini*, Leipzig, 1855–70. There are translations of Lucretius in English prose by H. A. J. Munro and Cyril Bailey, of which the first is famous for the austere grandeur of its style, while the latter (Oxford 1910), by the best living English scholar in this field, takes note of later advances in scholarship. Vitruvius can be read in English in Morgan's *Vitruvius: Ten Books on Architecture*, Harvard Univ. Press, 1926, and in English and Latin in the Loeb edition by Granger, 1931–4. For Frontinus the Loeb edition by Bennett is good. There is also a Loeb Celsus; the fundamental edition is by F. Marx, Leipzig, 1915, with Prolegomena in Latin. The best book on Pliny the Elder is *Histoire Naturelle de Pline, avec Traduction en Français*, par M. E. Littré, Paris, 1877. For Geminus see C. Manitius, *Gemini Elementa Astronomiae*, Leipzig, 1898. For Strabo there is a Loeb edition in eight vols., and an excellent account of Strabo's position in the history of his subject in Tozer, *History of Ancient Geography*, Cambridge, 1897. The articles on Ptolemy as astronomer and geographer by Allman and Bunbury in the Encycl. Br., 9th ed., are excellent. The mathematical works of Ptolemy can mostly be found in the Teubner ed., the geography in the Tauchnitz. For an admirable account of Galen see Singer's *Evolution of Anatomy*, Kegan Paul, 1925. The little work *On His Own Writings* quoted in our text can be found in Marquardt, Müller and Helmreich, *Galeni Scripta Minora*, Leipzig, 1884. Clifford Allbutt's *Greek Medicine in Rome* is rich in information and ideas. Brock, *Greek Medicine*, is a useful conspectus of the subject with many passages quoted in translation.

CHAPTER FOUR

Résumé and Conclusion – Achievement and limitations of ancient science – The debt of modern to ancient science.

★

RÉSUMÉ AND CONCLUSION

IN the foregoing pages we have given a representative selection from the scientific writings of the Alexandrian and Graeco-Roman periods. But our treatment has not been exhaustive. A fuller treatment would demand a higher degree of specialization in various branches of science than the present writer can claim to possess. But, while much more might be said, enough has perhaps been said to indicate the range and brilliance of the science of classical antiquity. With astonishment we find ourselves on the threshold of modern science. Nor should it be supposed that by some trick of translation the extracts have been given a delusive air of modernity. Far from it. The vocabulary of these writings and their style are the source from which our own vocabulary and style have been derived. There is no illusion here. With the science of Alexandria and of Rome we are in very truth on the threshold of the modern world. When modern science began in the sixteenth century it took up where the Greeks left off. Copernicus, Vesalius and Galileo are the continuators of Ptolemy, Galen and Archimedes.

But, if our first impression is favourable, it is quickly succeeded by a strange doubt. The Greeks and Romans stood on the threshold of the modern world. Why did they not push open the door? The situation is paradoxical in the extreme. We have here surveyed a period of some five hundred years, from the death of Aristotle in 322 B.C. to the death of Galen in A.D. 199. But long before the end of this period the essential work had been done. Before the end of the third century B.C. Theophrastus, Strato, Herophilus and Erasistratus, Ctesibius and Archimedes had done their work. In the Lyceum and the Museum the prosecution of research had reached a high degree of efficiency. The capacity to organize knowledge logically was great. The range of positive information was impressive, the rate of its acquisition more impressive still. The theory of experiment had been grasped. Applications of science to various ingenious mechanisms were not lacking. It was not, then, only with Ptolemy and Galen that the ancients stood on the threshold of the modern world. By that late date they had already been loitering on the threshold for four hundred years. They had indeed demonstrated conclusively their inability to cross it.

Here, then, we have evidence of a real paralysis of science. During four hundred years there had been, as we have seen, many extensions of knowledge, much reorganization of the body of knowledge, fresh acquisitions of skill in exposition. But there was no great forward drive, no general application of science to life. Science had ceased to be, or had failed to become, a real force in the life of society. Instead there had arisen a conception of science as a cycle of liberal studies for a privileged minority. Science had become a relaxation, an adornment, a subject of contemplation. It had ceased to be a means of transforming the conditions of life. Even such established arts as were adapted to keeping society in repair – professions like those of the architect and the medical doctor – were on the edge of respectability. They approached it only to the extent to which the practitioner could be regarded as the possessor of purely theoretical knowledge by which he directed the labour of others.

When we look for the causes of this paralysis it is obvious

that it is not due to any failure of the individual. The endeavour to explain great social movements by the psychology of individuals is one of the crippling errors of our time. No, while science as a whole became a prey to creeping paralysis, there was no lack of individual talent, no lack of individual genius, as these pages abundantly show. The failure was a social one and the remedy lay in public policies that were beyond the grasp of the age. The ancients rigorously organized the logical aspects of science, lifted them out of the body of technical activity in which they had grown or in which they should have found their application, and set them apart from the world of practice and above it. This mischievous separation of the logic from the practice of science was the result of the universal cleavage of society into freeman and slave. This was not good either for practice or for theory. As Francis Bacon put it, surveying according to the knowledge of his day the same facts that we have here surveyed, if you make a vestal virgin of science you must not expect her to bear fruit. The fruits of a general improvement in the material conditions of life and of a general emancipation of society from superstition were not such as could be produced by such a reverend maid as ancient science became in its decline.

With us to-day the concept of science carries with it the idea of a transforming power over the conditions of life. While we properly defend the ideal of science as involving a disinterested devotion to truth – indeed this ideal is itself a product of social history and has never shone more brightly than among those of our contemporaries who recognize and acknowledge the social responsibilities of scientific power – we recognize at the same time that from the well-head of pure science flow fertilizing streams which serve industry. We are nearly all Baconian enough to regard science as not only knowledge of nature but as power over nature. The complementary truth, that industry promotes science as much as science promotes industry, is also part of our usual view. The mutual action of science upon life and life upon science is a basic element in our consciousness. It was not so when antiquity was in its decline. Science was for the study and the few. Power over nature was increased, so long as this proved possible, by increasing the number of slaves.

ACHIEVEMENT AND LIMITATIONS OF ANCIENT SCIENCE

The failure of ancient science was in the use that was made of it. It failed in its social function. Even when the acquisition of slaves became more and more difficult the ancients still did not turn to a systematic application of science to production. It is not claimed that such applications never occurred. Bromehead, for instance, adduces evidence which serves to modify Neuburger's conclusion that 'the art of mining appears to have made almost no technical progress during the whole of antiquity, that is, from the date of the earliest traces recorded to the fall of the Roman Empire'.[1] But the general truth remains that ancient society had set in a mould which precluded the possibility of an effective search for power other than the muscles of slaves. The dependence of society on the slave is everywhere reflected in the consciousness of the age. For Plato and Aristotle in the fourth century B.C. it was axiomatic that civilization could not exist without slaves. Three hundred years later, although slaves had become much more difficult to catch, the Alexandrian philosopher Philo is still of the same opinion. Life without slaves

1. *The Evidence for Ancient Mining* by C. E. N. Bromehead. The *Geographical Journal*, Vol. XCVI, no. 2, August, 1940. The reference is to Neuburger's *Technical Arts and Sciences of the Ancients*, London, 1930, p. 7.

being unthinkable, he draws the conclusion (he was an earnest moralist) that the moral law permits the acquisition of slaves. His rules for their treatment, intended like those of Plato to be just and humanitarian, sufficiently reveal the repressed bad conscience and the horrible social reality. He provides that a master who kills a slave should be killed, but adds that 'if the slave lives two days after being flogged' the master should be acquitted.

Philo was born in 25 B.C., but even after some centuries of Christianity society was still set in the same mould. St Augustine (A.D. 354–430) accepted slavery as the judgment of God on a world guilty of original sin. These opinions, pagan and Christian, are not an index to the character of individuals but to the character of the times. The slow operation of historical forces had brought about the slave system. Only powerful historical forces could sweep it away. The nature of these forces, and the slow change they effected in the mind of society, have been well described by Engels. 'Slavery', he writes in *The Origin of the Family*, 'no longer paid; it was for that reason it died out. But in dying it left behind its poisoned sting – the stigma attached to the productive labour of freemen. This was the blind alley from which the Roman world had no way out: slavery was economically impossible, the labour of freemen was morally ostracized. The one could be the basic form of social production no longer; the other, not yet. Nothing could help here except a complete revolution.' That revolution, the work of the northern barbarians, took place between A.D. 400 and 800. 'Though at the end', continues Engels, 'we find almost the same classes as at the beginning, the human beings who formed these classes were different. Ancient slavery had gone, and so had the pauper freeman who despised work as only fit for slaves. Between the Roman *colonus* and the new bondsman had stood the free Frankish peasant. The "useless memories and aimless strife" of decadent Roman culture were dead and buried. The social classes of the ninth century had been formed, not in the rottenness of a decaying civilization, but in the birth-pangs of a new civilization.'

This new civilization, arising out of the grave of slave society, soon flowered in a series of new inventions which transformed the economic basis of life. In an article in *Le Mercure de France* (May, 1932) Des Noëttes offered a brief inventory of the chief inventions of the Middle Ages. He includes the watermill, which was known to antiquity but apparently little used.[2] This is his list:

IX century – The modern harness of the saddle-horse, with saddle, stirrups, bit, and nailed iron shoes.

X century – The modern harness of the draft-animal, with shoulder-collar, shafts, disposition in file and nailed shoes.

XII century – Watermill, windmill, mechanical saw, forge with tilt-hammer, bellows with stiff boards and valve, window-glass and glazed windows, the domestic chimney, candle and taper, paved roads,[3] the wheel-barrow.

XIII century – Spectacles, wheeled-plough with mould-board, rudder.[4]

XIV century – Lock-gates on canals, gunpowder, grandfather-clock, plane.

XV century – Printing.

2. His inclusion of the plane is also open to question. Museums show Roman examples.

3. As distinct from the Roman practice of constructing a massive wall of masonry in a trench three or four feet deep and using the top as a road. See Des Noëttes, *L'Attelage, le cheval de salle, à travers les âges. Contribution à l'histoire de l'esclavage,* Paris, 1931; also R. J. Forbes, *Notes on the History of Ancient Roads and their Construction,* Amsterdam, 1934.

4. As distinct from the ancient steering-oar.

In another of his writings, a masterpiece of research and of historical analysis,[5] Des Noëttes discusses the social consequences of this series of inventions. He is not wrong when he insists that 'by fundamentally transforming the means of production they fundamentally transformed the social organism'. Nor is his conclusion lessened in importance when we understand that one of the transformations of the social organism involved was the disappearance of the last vestiges of slavery and the possibility of undertaking immense constructional works with free labour – works of a kind which had normally been performed in antiquity by the forced labour of slaves. This implied an immense improvement in the consciousness of the modern world over the ancient. For, as Des Noëttes remarks, 'the ancients in reality knew nothing of the rights of man; those of the citizen were all that existed for them'.

The same point has been taken up more recently by an American enquirer, whose conclusions are worth quoting here.[6] 'The cumulative effect of the newly available animal, water and wind power upon the culture of Europe has not been carefully studied. But from the twelfth and even from the eleventh century there was a rapid replacement of human by non-human energy wherever great quantities of power were needed or where the required motion was so simple and monotonous that a man could be replaced by a mechanism. The chief glory of the later Middle Ages was not its cathedrals or its epics or its scholasticism: it was the building for the first time in history of a complex civilization which rested not on the backs of sweating slaves or coolies but primarily on non-human power.'

5. *Op. cit.,* note 3 above.

6. Lynn White, Jr., *Technology and Invention in the Middle Ages,* Speculum, XV, 1940, pp. 141ff.

It has been naïvely taught, and is still sometimes naïvely believed, that the science of the Renaissance arose because Greek books from Constantinople arrived in western Europe. If this were the whole truth of the matter, we might well ask why the modern world was not born in Alexandria, or in Rome, or in Constantinople, where the old books survived. There is another aspect of the truth to be considered. Graeco-Roman science was good seed, but it could not grow on the stony ground of ancient slave society. The technical revolution of the Middle Ages was necessary to prepare the soil of western Europe to receive the seed, and the technical device of printing was necessary to multiply and broadcast the seed before the ancient wisdom could raise a wholesome crop.

The point has been admirably made by Professor Fawcett.[7] 'The peoples of western Europe had the advantage of living in a region where three of the important natural resources for the simpler forms of power were more abundant than in the lands of the older civilizations. The climate gave them more continuous vegetation, and thus allowed them to have more work-animals ; it also gave them wind enough at all seasons to drive the ships on their seas and simple windmills on land ; and the abundance of rain, combined with the absence of a dry season, enabled them to have widespread small-scale water-power on their streams. Thus, when they had learned how to make use of these resources, they built up a society in which humans were freed from a large part of the necessary drudgery. These technical advances led to social changes ; for the chattel slave and the galley slave were no longer needed, and those crude forms of compulsory labour slowly disappeared. They were replaced partly by serfdom and partly by the organizations of craftsmen ; both of

7. *The Basis of a World Commonwealth*, Watts, 1941, p. 3.

which merged later into the wage system of modern capitalistic democracy.'

THE DEBT OF MODERN TO ANCIENT SCIENCE

The creators of modern science in the sixteenth century, working again in an age of technical advance in which ancient social abuses were being swept away, recapture the humanitarian as well as the scientific zeal of old Ionia. Reading their pages we seem to breathe a purer and freer air. When Plato wrote his Utopias he was haunted by the necessity of repressing a servile labour force. In St Thomas More's *Utopia* the workers are free men and society is organized in their interest. 'The chief end of the constitution is to regulate labour by the needs of the commonweal, and to allow the people as much time as is necessary for the improvement of their minds, in which they think the happiness of life consists.' It should not be overlooked what a novel conception this is of a labour force with mental needs and joys. In Plato's analogy between man and society the rulers had been equated with the head, the police with the chest, and the workers with the belly and the loins.

In the literature of this age the new temper finds frequent expression. Whereas Archimedes had expressed his contempt for the useful applications of science, Simon Stevin (1548–1620), who is known as the Archimedes of the Low Countries, is anxious above all to be useful. Introducing his decimal system of notation to the public he says humbly : 'It is not a great invention, but it is eminently useful to everyone.'

Where in antiquity shall we find a learned treatise on mining? In the middle of the sixteenth century appeared the *De Re Metallica* of Agricola, in which the whole process of the extraction of minerals is expounded. It is an education to read in his opening pages the list of the basic sciences he considers necessary for this industry. The connection between an actively developing theory and its practical applications is disclosed in a manner characteristic of the modern world but foreign to ancient science in its decline. Not less admirable than his descriptions of machines and processes is his defence of the social utility of the industry.

Soon chemistry too, which in antiquity had lived an underground existence because its practitioners – the fullers, the dyers, the glass-makers, the potters, the compounders of drugs – were outlawed from society, began to assert its claims to be an honoured science with many protestations on the part of its pioneers that it was no occupation for those who were too proud to dirty their hands. Chemistry is a subject we have neglected in this volume, its origins being unusually obscure. But that the difficulties this science experienced in trying to get born were social rather than inherent in the nature of the matter to be investigated is suggested as much by the writings of Bolos Democritus (c. 200 B.C.) in antiquity as by those of John Rudolph Glauber (1604–70) in modern times.

Glauber, like Agricola, had a lively sense of the contribution science could make to life.[8] When this aspect of science came again to the fore, it was not long before the effect of the industrial applications of science on the health of the workers forced itself upon the attention. This effect had been observed but neglected in antiquity, when slaves and condemned criminals were sent to the quarries and the mines, and dangerous trades in general were not the serious concern of governments. The Hippocratic doctors had written of the effect of the *environment* on health, but they considered only the *natural* environment. It remained for the modern world to discover that the most important aspect of

8. He assessed the technical possibilities of Germany in an acute and comprehensive way.

the environment for the worker is the job. Paracelsus (1490–1541) is the first to draw attention to this gap in the medical theory of antiquity. Discussing the dreadful effects of their trades on miners and metal-workers, the asthmas, consumptions and vomitings, he comments : 'There is absolutely nothing about these diseases to be found in the ancient medical tradition, whence, up to the present day, no remedy is known.' These conclusions were later extended to almost all known occupations by the great Ramazzini (1633–1714), whose classic work *De Morbis Artificum* rivals the merits and exceeds the humanity of the greatest works of antiquity.

Perhaps the most decisive defeat of the scientific spirit in antiquity had been the loss of the sense of history. History is the most fundamental science, for there is no human knowledge which cannot lose its scientific character when men forget the conditions under which it originated, the questions which it answered, and the function it was created to serve. A great part of the mysticism and superstition of educated men consists of knowledge which has broken loose from its historical moorings. It is for this reason that we have stressed the sketches of civilization given by Democritus and Lucretius and characterized them as the most important achievement of ancient science.

The process by which the knowledge of one generation can be transformed into the superstition of the next can conveniently be studied by passing from the *De Rerum Natura* of Lucretius to the *Aeneid* of Virgil. It can also be studied in what the learning of Alexandria made of the Hebrew scriptures when they were translated into Greek. It might have been expected that the addition to Greek literature of the historical record of a strange people would deepen their historical sense. In fact the historical interpretation of the Hebrew scriptures is a product of recent times. The classical world had turned its own history into myth before it acquired a knowledge of the Old Testament and it treated it unhistorically from the first. It would hardly be possible to be more learned than Origen (A.D. 186–254), who applied all the resources of Alexandrian scholarship to the work of biblical criticism. But in the absence of any historical sense it is admitted that his interpretations are entirely arbitrary. What history lost theology gained, and human history dwindled to the proportions of a small act in a cosmic drama. The real events were the Revolt of the Angels, the Creation, the Fall, the Redemption, the Millennium and the Last Judgment. Lost in these mysteries time shrank to the limits of six thousand years and human history had significance only in relation to the transcendental framework within which it was contained.

The greatest achievement of modern science has been the rebirth of the historical sense. This is a subject on which we cannot enter here, but a brief allusion to it will form the appropriate conclusion to our book. We have mentioned the names of some of the great founders of modern science – Copernicus, Vesalius, Galileo, Stevin, and others. The man who gave supreme expression to the spirit of this age was the Englishman, Francis Bacon (1561–1626). He turned on the whole question of the revival of science an acute historical sense, remarkable for his day and little understood by his successors. The body of the Baconian writings constitutes one great comment on human history, the sense of which is that the real history of humanity can only be written in terms of man's conquest over his environment. His subject was, in his own words, The Interpretation of Nature and Man's Dominion over it. He penetrated behind the veil of politics to the economic reality and judged man's past achievement and future prospects in terms of his mastery over nature, not denying other aspects of his culture but relating them to this basic fact.

The sense of the reality of time, the reality of historical change, and the influence exercised by man over his own destiny, were contributions to the profound philosophy of Vico (1668–1744), who, in the light of his intuition that Man makes his own History, was justified in his claim to have made of history The New Science. Bacon glimpsed the truth that man makes his mental history in the process of conquering his world. Vico saw more clearly than Bacon that this is not an achievement of individual man but of society. In the fundamental institutions of human society he saw the instruments whereby man, who began as a brute, has transformed himself into a civilized being. Later philosophers, notably Hegel and Marx, have deepened and developed these ideas until they have become precious tools for man by which he can consciously labour at the amelioration of his own society. In the light of these conceptions the history of science assumes a new importance. It becomes, not the history of one among several branches of human knowledge, but the essential clue to the process by which man achieves his self-transformation from the animal to the human kingdom. It is in the conviction that the better understanding of any stage in this long journey must contribute to the attainment of the final goal that this study has been written.

BIBLIOGRAPHICAL NOTE

For a general account of ancient technique especially in the Alexandrian Age see Diels, *Antike Technik*, 3rd ed., Leipzig, 1924. The essential studies on Bolos Democritus are by Wellman in *Abhandlungen der Preussischen Akademie, Philosophisch-Historische Klasse*, 1921, No. 4, and 1928, No. 7. For the revival of historical studies in modern times, see R. G. Collingwood, *Autobiography* (Pelican) and *Vico : His Autobiography*, by Fisch and Bergin, 1945.

INDEX

SOME
PENGUIN
PUBLICATIONS

SOME NEW PELICANS

None of these titles has appeared in any other form

—

A Short History of English Drama
B. IFOR EVANS
A172

This author's *Short History of English Literature,* one of the most successful of Pelicans, is now followed by a similar survey of English Drama. It covers the whole development from the Middle Ages to modern times and will prove an indispensable guide to all students professional or otherwise.

The Life of Jesus
C. J. CADOUX
A189

The author was a distinguished theologian who had just finished writing this book when he died in 1947. His aim was to make a fresh survey of the facts about the life and work of Jesus and to interpret – without any flights of fancy – the significance of his mission. The result is a fascinating and persuasive biography.

The Size of the Universe
F. J. HARGREAVES
A193

This book has been written for those many thousands of people who would like to study astronomy on a basis which does not involve an elaborate knowledge of mathematics. They will find exactly what they want in this vivid and straightforward introduction to one of the most attractive of the sciences.

The Population of Britain
EVA M. HUBBACK
A174

In the task of rebuilding after the war, no factor is more fundamental to the people of Britain than the size and quality of its population.

Population trends are intimately bound up with most of the economic, social and political issues of the day. Is our population to drop or to remain stable? What changes in our lives will be occasioned by an increase in the proportion of older people? What classes of the population should be encouraged to have larger families, and what steps are desirable and possible to give that encouragement?

All these questions are discussed by the author, and a practical population policy is suggested on the basis of the trends which statistics indicate as existing or likely to exist in the near future.

Mrs Hubback's work is especially timely in view of the appointment of the Royal Commission on Population, whose report is anticipated in the near future.

Genetics

H. KALMUS, SC.D., and LETTICE M. CRUMP, M.SC.

A179

Though genetics is the youngest of the biological sciences, it is exciting more attention at the present time than any other branch of biological inquiry.

It has grown so fast, and in so spectacular a manner, that the majority of scientists cannot keep abreast of it; in consequence it has won an undeserved reputation for being difficult to understand. How undeserved, will be apparent to every reader of this book: for Dr Kalmus and his collaborator here set out in simple language the main principles of the science so clearly and concisely that every reader will be able to follow them.

What factors of biological make-up are inherited, in plants, animals and man; how they are inherited; how mutations and variations arise and are transmitted; the importance of genetical knowledge to the gardener, farmer, stockbreeder, and human parent: all these matters are discussed and explained, and the text is elucidated by a number of simple diagrams.

The Personality of Man
G. N. M. TYRRELL
A165

' The Personality of Man can be recommended as a soberly expert survey of psychical research up to date ... Is all this worth while? Surely yes; our command of external nature is grotesquely and dangerously out of step with our knowledge of the subjective realms of human nature. Psychical research has shown that these realms are strange and far-reaching; we are fumbling on the frontiers of a new continent.' – Charles Davy in *The Observer*.

' An immense amount of very readable information and comment on every aspect of the "paranormal".' – *Times Literary Supplement*.

' The president of the Society for Psychical Research has given us an important Pelican book ... with materialism no longer in the ascendancy people are becoming aware that psychical research is a respectable science.' – *The Guardian*.

' The cases he cites provide a formidable quantity of evidence that the subconscious can foresee the shape of things to come.' – *The Irish Times*.

The Bleak Age
J. L. and BARBARA HAMMOND
A171

The first half of the nineteenth century may well be named 'The Bleak Age' or 'The Age of Discontent'.

In this acute study the Hammonds illumine the dark places in the lives and hearts of the working people of that time, and by brilliant comparison with the conditions of other times bring out the underlying causes of this discontent.

This is a wise book and one to be read by all who wish to understand the root causes of our social troubles, and so be the better able to judge the many remedies that are to-day being put forward for the future ordering of this country.

' This is not history without comment. The authors point to leisure as it is used in our own day. They quote and discuss Rostovtzeff's searching question, "Is not every civilization bound to decay as soon as it begins to penetrate the masses?" This Pelican edition rearranges, with fresh materials added, the fascinating book which first appeared in 1934. No finer short introduction to the last century in England could be named.' – *The Times*.

Plato and His Dialogues
G. LOWES DICKINSON
A155

'One of the ripest and most humane minds in Europe is that of Mr Lowes Dickinson ... his book on Plato is one which everyone ready to approach the greatest of the Greeks without scholarship but with simple interest in a human story should get and devour.' – *Star*.

'Again and again he makes us look at our own age while he speaks of another age. It is a most remarkable book.' – *Listener*.

Human Physiology
KENNETH WALKER
A102

Most of us know too little of the way our bodies work, and are liable in that state of comparative ignorance to become the victims of groundless anxieties about ourselves. In this compact and authoritative survey Mr Kenneth Walker sets forth in plain language the most up-to-date knowledge on the functioning of the human body, and reminds us too how profoundly the mind influences the working of the body.

Starting from the cell, the basis of human as of all life, he describes the nature and work of the digestive, circulatory, excretory, locomotor and nervous systems: the part that food plays in our lives; how we breathe: the functions of the special senses and the physiology of sensation; the chemistry of the body and the glandular system; and the processes of reproduction. A number of sketches in the text illustrate special points.

This book, specially written for the Pelican series, is now in its third large printing.

AN IMPORTANT REPRINT

—

Religion and the Rise of Capitalism

R. H. TAWNEY

Pelican A23

Religion and the Rise of Capitalism is a study of religious thought
on social issues during the three centuries from the later Middle
Ages to the early eighteenth century. Starting with an account of
mediaeval theories of social ethics, it goes on to examine the impact on traditional doctrines of the new forces released by the
economic and political changes of the age of the Reformation. The
social backgrounds and teaching of Luther, Calvin, and the English divines from Latimer to Laud, receive attention in turn. A
chapter on the Puritan Movement discusses, among other topics,
the theory that Capitalism had Puritanism as one of its parents.
The conclusion reached by the author at the end of his survey is
that 'the criticism which dismisses the concern of Churches with
economic relations and social organization as a modern innovation
finds little support in past history. What requires explanation is
not the view that these matters are part of the province of religion,
but the view that they are not'. While the book is primarily concerned with changes in the world of thought, it is not confined to
them. Holding that theories, in order to be understood, must be
read in the light of the practical realities which help to produce
them, it devotes part of its space to a consideration of the latter. It
attempts to explain the conditions which gave point to prohibi-
tions of usury and to the insistence on a just price; describes the
social consequences of the Tudor land question; and touches on
the impetus to economic speculation given by the price-revolution,
the expansion of foreign commerce, and the growth of the money-
market.

A NEW VENTURE

—

Under an agreement which has been made between Penguin Books and five leading publishers – Chatto & Windus, Faber & Faber, Hamish Hamilton, Heinemann, and Michael Joseph – Penguins have the first opportunity of reprinting some of their books, many by authors who have not appeared in Penguins before. The first two groups of titles in this scheme, and their previous publishers, are given here.

I

Commando *by Deneys Reitz* from Faber & Faber
The Horse's Mouth *by Joyce Cary* from Michael Joseph
Selected Poems *by T. S. Eliot* from Faber & Faber
My Life and Hard Times *by James Thurber* from Hamish Hamilton
Cakes and Ale *by Somerset Maugham* from Heinemann
The Big Sleep *by Raymond Chandler* from Hamish Hamilton
Odd Man Out *by F. L. Green* from Michael Joseph
Antic Hay *by Aldous Huxley* from Chatto & Windus
Angel Pavement *by J. B. Priestley* from Heinemann
Eminent Victorians *by Lytton Strachey* from Chatto & Windus

II

Hotel Splendide *by Ludwig Bemelmans* from Hamish Hamilton
The Smith of Smiths *by Hesketh Pearson* from Hamish Hamilton
Sons and Lovers *by D. H. Lawrence* from Heinemann
Hassan *by James Elroy Flecker* from Heinemann
The Sailor's Return and Beany-Eye *by David Garnett* from Chatto & Windus
The Journal of a Disappointed Man *by W. N. P. Barbellion* from Chatto & Windus
Looking for a Bluebird *by Joseph Wechsberg* from Michael Joseph
No Bed for Bacon *by Caryl Brahms and S. J. Simon* from Michael Joseph
Music Ho! *by Constant Lambert* from Faber & Faber
Sherston's Progress *by Siegfried Sassoon* from Faber & Faber

AGATHA CHRISTIE

—

In August, 1948, a million Agatha Christie books are being published in Penguins by special arrangement with Messrs Collins, the original publishers. Ten titles have been selected and they are:

PERIL AT END HOUSE

THE SITTAFORD MYSTERY

MURDER ON THE ORIENT EXPRESS

APPOINTMENT WITH DEATH

THE SEVEN DIALS MYSTERY

THE MURDER OF ROGER ACKROYD

THE MYSTERY OF THE BLUE TRAIN

THE ABC MURDERS

MURDER AT THE VICARAGE

LORD EDGWARE DIES

The Press on Agatha Christie:

'The best of all crime novelists.' – *Bystander*.

'She has held the throne of detection for the last ten years and brooks no rival near her.' – *New Statesman*.

'The most subtle and ingenious writer of crime fiction alive to-day.' – *News Chronicle*.

'Agatha Christie and Hercule Poirot, the best combination in modern detective literature.' – *Time and Tide*.

'She gives the highly enjoyable impression that both she and the reader are taking part in a mutually exciting game.' – *London Mercury*.

THE PENGUIN CLASSICS

A LIBRARY OF NEW TRANSLATIONS

EDITED BY E. V. RIEU

—

HOMER
THE ODYSSEY
Translated by E. V. Rieu

'He catches the directness and simplicity and poise of the original better than any previous translator.' – *The Listener.*

MAUPASSANT
BOULE DE SUIF AND OTHER STORIES
Translated by H. N. P. Sloman

'The translation has been admirably done.' – *The Scotsman.*

SOPHOCLES
THE THEBAN PLAYS
Translated by E. F. Watling

'Mr Watling is to be congratulated not only on the lucidity and sound scholarship of the translation but on his success in enabling the reader to grasp the character of these great dramas and the atmosphere in which they were first enacted.' – *Free Verse.*

VOLTAIRE
CANDIDE
Translated by John Butt

'Mr Butt has given a pleasing modern English translation, and an informative introduction on Voltaire's work, his aims, and the factual basis of CANDIDE.' – *British Book News.*

Other volumes are in preparation